SEATING CHARTS FOR MINNESOTA ARENAS, AUDITORIUMS AND THEATRES

Seat Yourself

D1597288

ADVENTURE PUBLICATIONS, Inc.
P.O. Box 269, Cambridge, Minnesota 55008
1-800-678-7006
First printing . . . September 1988
Second printing . . . August 1990
Third printing . . . October 1991
ISBN 0-934860-75-0

Also by Marlys Mickelson
BIKING IN VIKINGLAND

Cover Design — Ralph Brown, Jack of Arts — Elysian, Minnesota

Front cover photos — World Theater (Courtesy of the World Theater, George Heinrich, photographer. St. Paul Civic Center (Courtesy of the St. Paul Convention and Visitors Bureau) Northrup Dance Season (Courtesy of the Minnesota Office of Tourism) Minnesota Vikings (Photo courtesy of the Vikings)

Back cover photo — Hubert H. Humphrey Metrodome (Courtesy of the Minnesota Office of Tourism)

Request information on elevators/escalators/physically disadvantaged access from box office reservationist.

This book provides charts of the most common seating arrangements.
Individual promoters may modify seating for specific performances or events.

CONTENTS

CHANHASSEN DINNER THEATRES

ADDRESS: 501 West 78th Street
Chanhassen, MN 55317

TICKETS: 612-934-1525 Box Office
1-800-362-3515 five state toll-free

SEATING
CAPACITY: Main Dinner Theatre 546

Fireside Theatre 254

Dinner Playhouse 130

Seating arrangements may be subject to adjustment for specific productions.

SEASON: Open throughout the year

HISTORY: Founded in 1968, boasting multiple theatres under one roof, Chanhassen Dinner Theatres is considered the largest professional dinner theatre complex in the nation. The Main Dinner Theatre and Fireside both have reserved seating. The Dinner Playhouse, seating 130 has flexible seating and guests are placed according to their reservation order date. Recently, the Courtyard Theatre was converted into a new night spot called CLUB CHAN featuring live entertainment.

PARKING: Free parking ample parking

CHANHASSEN DINNER THEATRES

MAIN DINNER THEATRE

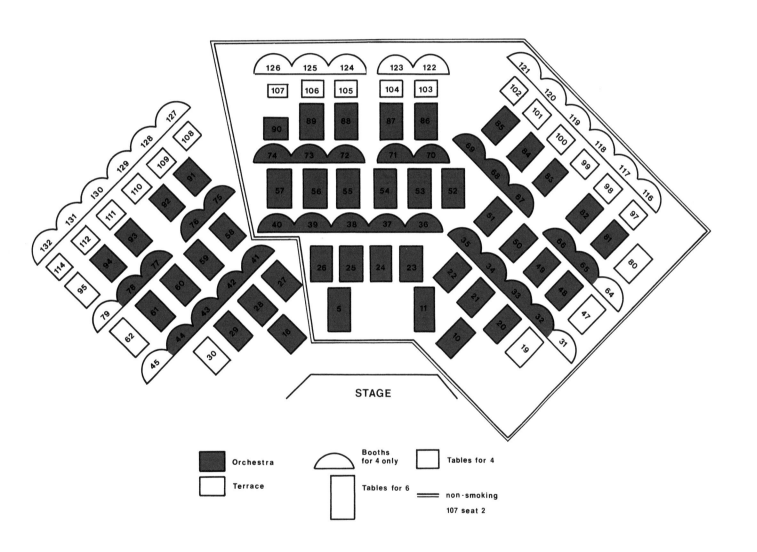

THE CHILDREN'S THEATRE COMPANY

ADDRESS: 2400 Third Avenue South
Minneapolis, MN 55404

TICKETS: 612-874-0400

SEATING
CAPACITY: 746

SEASON: September through June
Seven shows per season

HISTORY: Founded in 1965, the Children's Theatre Company used the auditorium/lecture hall of the Minneapolis Institute of Arts until 1974 when they moved into their new theatre and educational facility adjacent to, but no longer affiliated with the Minneapolis Society of Fine Arts.

The Children's Theatre Company is the largest children's theatre in this country and the fifth largest youth theatre in the world.

PARKING: Parking is free in the ramp directly behind the theatre.

THE CHILDREN'S THEATRE COMPANY

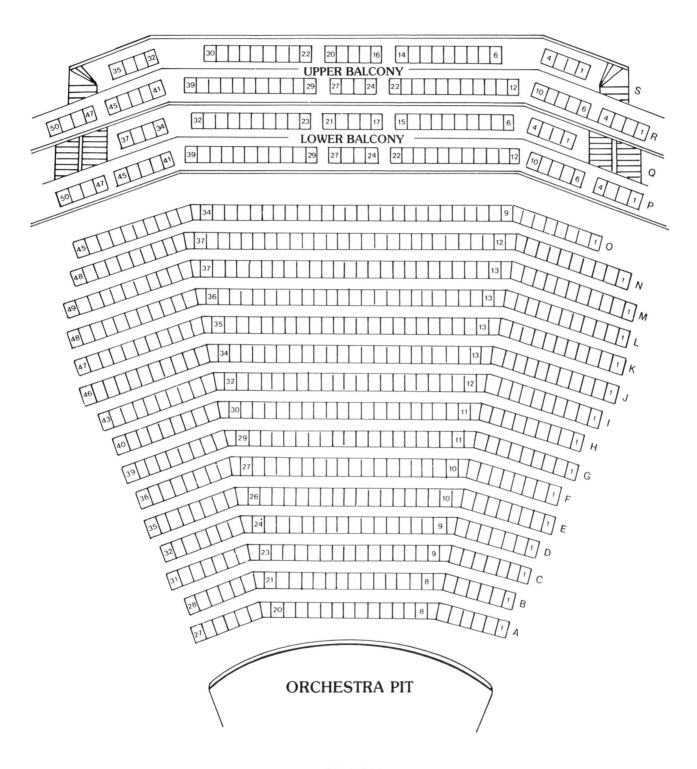

ORCHESTRA PIT

STAGE

ST. PAUL CIVIC CENTER ARENA

ADDRESS: I.A. O'Shaughnessey Plaza
Seventh Street and Kellogg Boulevard
St. Paul, MN 55102

TICKETS: 612-224-7403

**SEATING
CAPACITY:** Arena, 18,000 for concerts
Wilkins, 3,700 permanent seats
5,700 performance or special event

SEASON: Open throughout the year

HISTORY: The Civic Center is a multi-purpose arena with
special events including: concerts, ice shows,
hockey, wrestling, fights and basketball.

Annually hosts the largest high school sports
event in the nation, the Minnesota State High
School Hockey Tournament.

Roy Wilkins Auditorium has four major function/
event areas: Lower Level Exhibit Hall, Auditorium
Main Level, Ballroom, and Executive Meeting
Room. It is frequently used for political and
other conventions.

PARKING: A 1600-vehicle parking ramp with walkway off
Kellogg Boulevard to the south of the arena.
Also, a number of adjacent public parking lots.

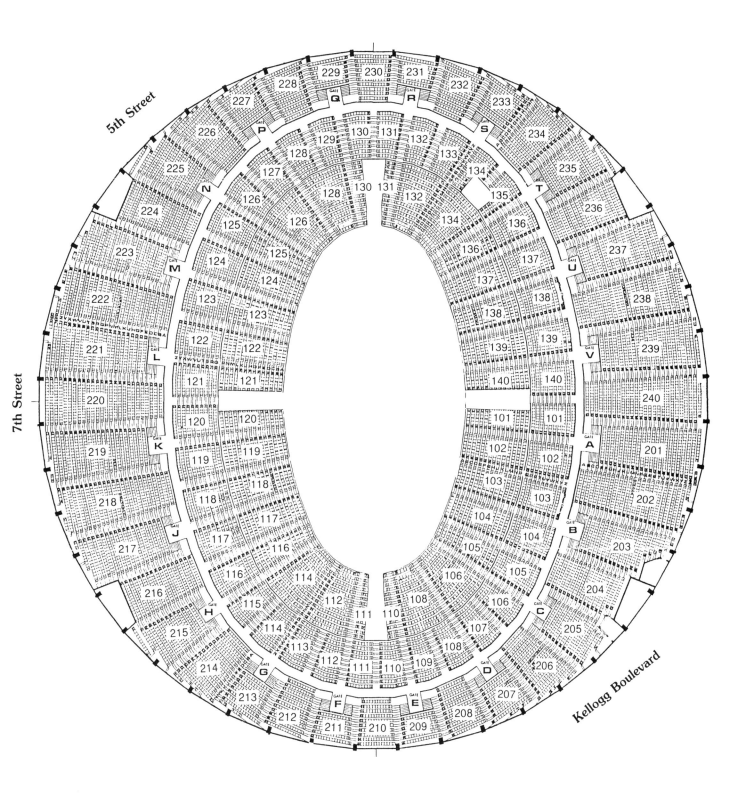

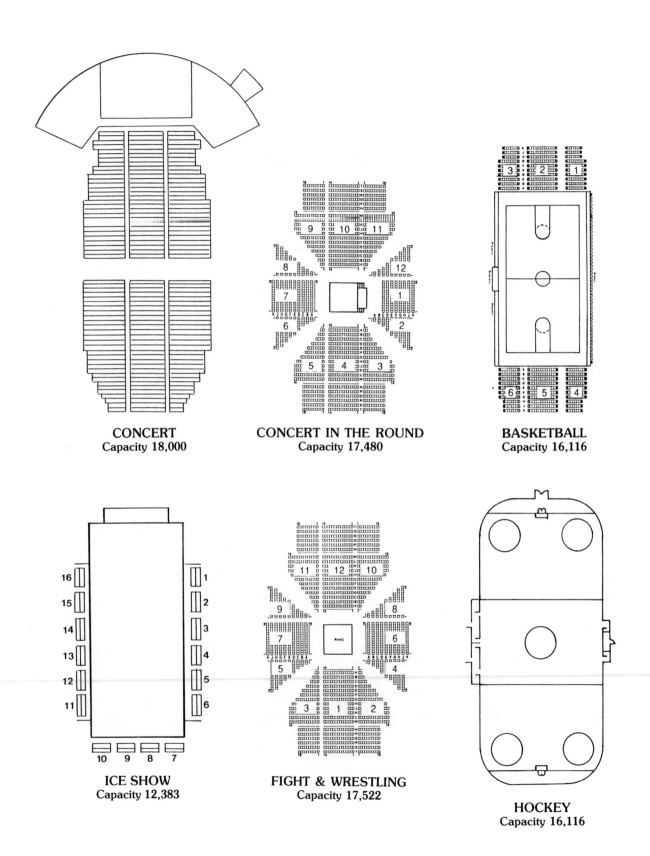

CONCERT
Capacity 18,000

CONCERT IN THE ROUND
Capacity 17,480

BASKETBALL
Capacity 16,116

ICE SHOW
Capacity 12,383

FIGHT & WRESTLING
Capacity 17,522

HOCKEY
Capacity 16,116

ROY WILKINS AUDITORIUM

MAIN FLOOR
BLEACHERS

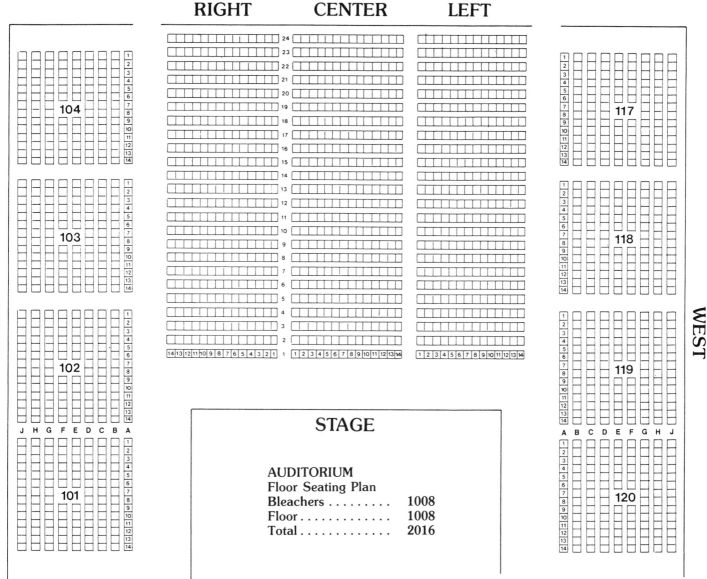

RIGHT   CENTER   LEFT

EAST

WEST

STAGE

AUDITORIUM
Floor Seating Plan
Bleachers   1008
Floor   1008
Total   2016

MAIN FLOOR

CHAIRS

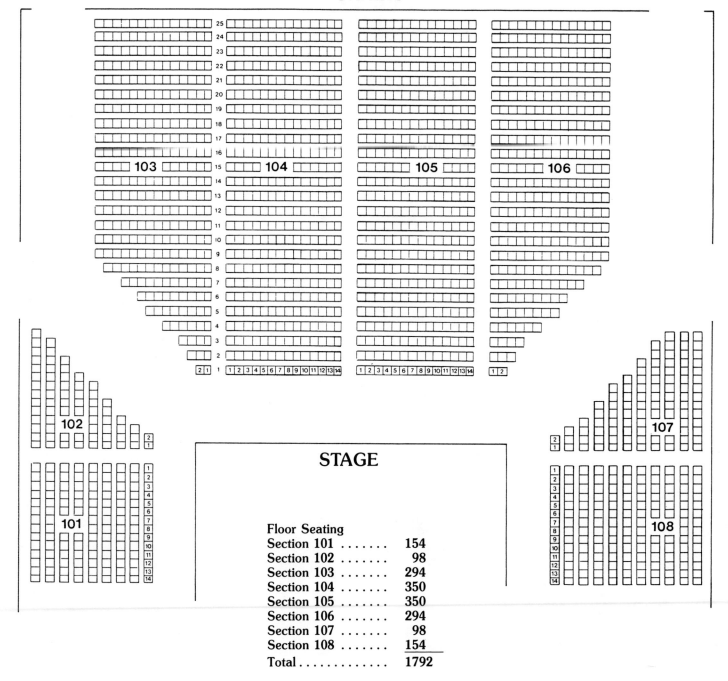

STAGE

Floor Seating
Section 101   154
Section 102   98
Section 103   294
Section 104   350
Section 105   350
Section 106   294
Section 107   98
Section 108   154
Total 1792

BALCONY

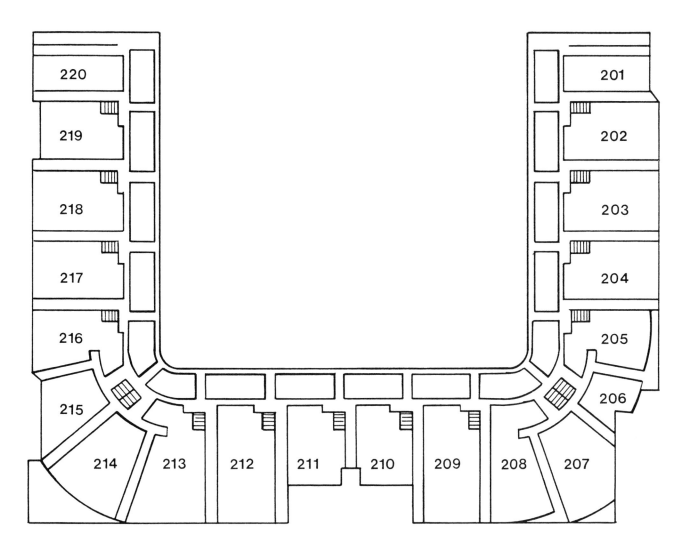

CRICKET THEATRE

ADDRESS: 1407 Nicollet Avenue
                    Minneapolis, MN 55403

TICKETS: 612-871-2244

SEATING
CAPACITY: 213

SEASON: Fall portion of season opens in September and
                    continues into November.

                    Spring portion of season opens in February and
                    continues into June.

                    The Cricket Theatre's annual holiday concert
                    opens in November or December and continues
                    through the holiday season. A variety of extra-
                    seasonal concerts, plays, and special events are
                    scheduled at the Cricket Theatre throughout
                    the year.

                    The Cricket Theatre is available for rental and
                    is used by performing arts groups and other
                    organizations including the New Dance Ensem-
                    ble and Sequoia Theatre Company.

HISTORY: The Cricket Theatre was founded in 1971, first
                    performed at the Ritz Theatre in northeast
                    Minneapolis and then at the Hennepin Center
                    for the Arts. The theatre moved to its Nicollet
                    Avenue location in March, 1987.

PARKING: Parking is available at the Loring Municipal
                    Ramp (one block north of the theatre on Nicol-
                    let Avenue).

CRICKET THEATRE

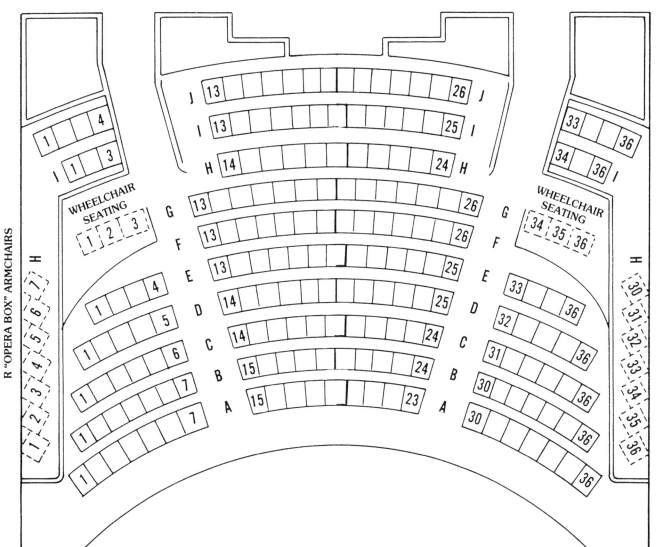

DULUTH ENTERTAINMENT CONV. CTR.

ADDRESS: 350 Harbor Drive
Duluth, Minnesota 55802

TICKETS: 218-727-4344

SEATING
CAPACITY: Auditorium 2400
Arena 8000

SEASON: Open throughout the year

HISTORY: The auditorium opened in 1966 and is part of a multi-purpose complex consisting of an 8,000 seat arena, over 100,000 sq. ft. of exhibit space and the recent addition of 127,000 sq. ft. convention center. DECC hosts a variety of events including hockey, concerts, wrestling, trade shows, conventions, symphony and a number of broadway shows.

PARKING: Parking for 1360 vehicles in adjacent parking lot. A fee is charged.

The complex is connected to downtown Duluth by a skywalk system.

DECC

AUDITORIUM

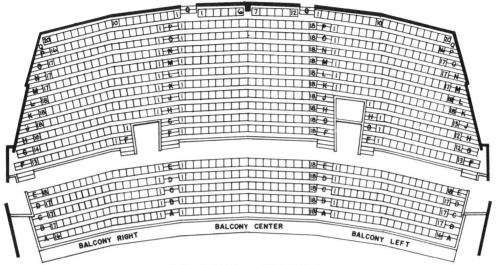

BALCONY   SEATING

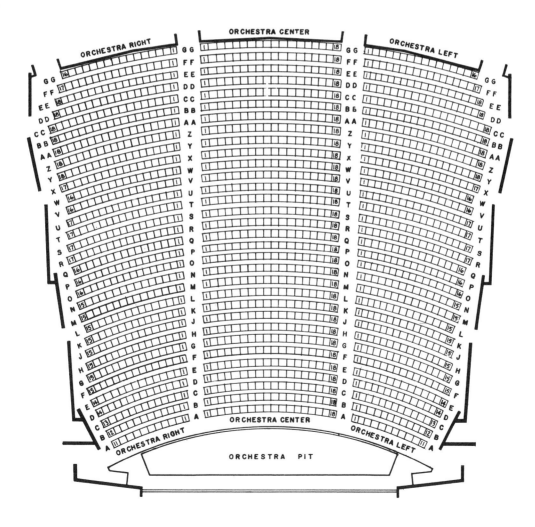

ARENA ICE SHOW

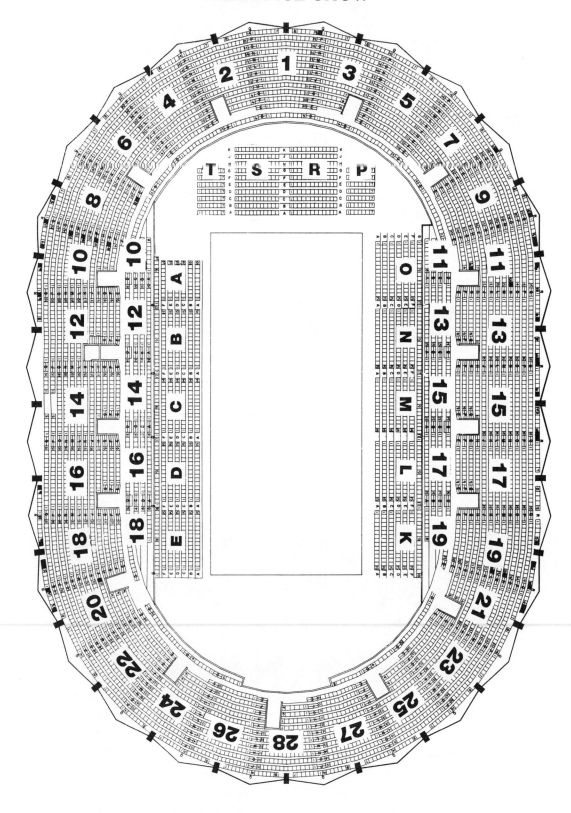

DECC

CONCERT

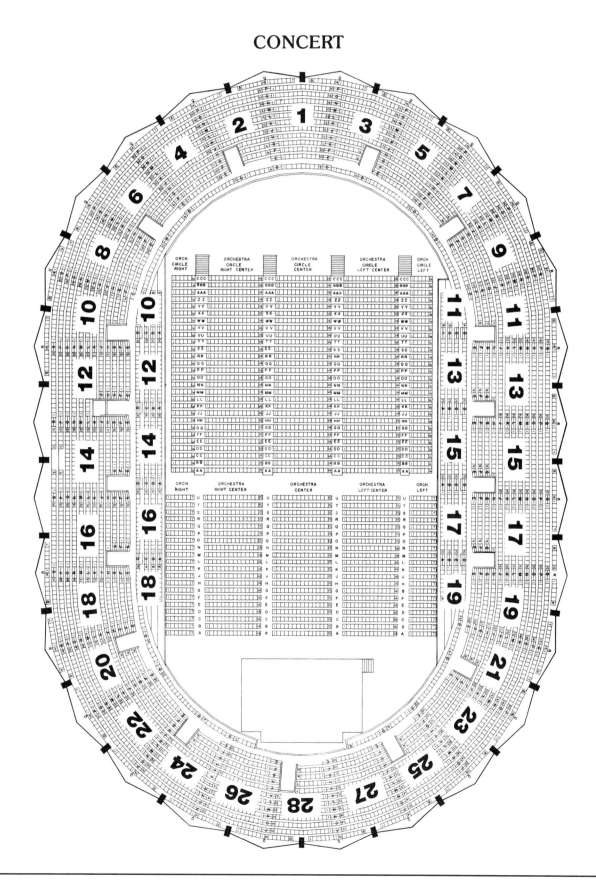

GREAT N. AMER. HISTORY THEATRE

ADDRESS: 30 East Tenth Street
St. Paul, MN 55101

TICKETS: 612-292-4323

SEATING
CAPACITY: 597

SEASON: September through May

HISTORY: The History Theatre started in the Weyerhaeuser Auditorium, Landmark Center in 1977,
moving to its present quarters in the fall of
1988.

The History Theatre premieres new plays by
contemporary writers that connect us to our
past and the future.

PARKING: Science Museum of Minnesota parking ramp on
10th between Wabasha St. and St. Peter St.

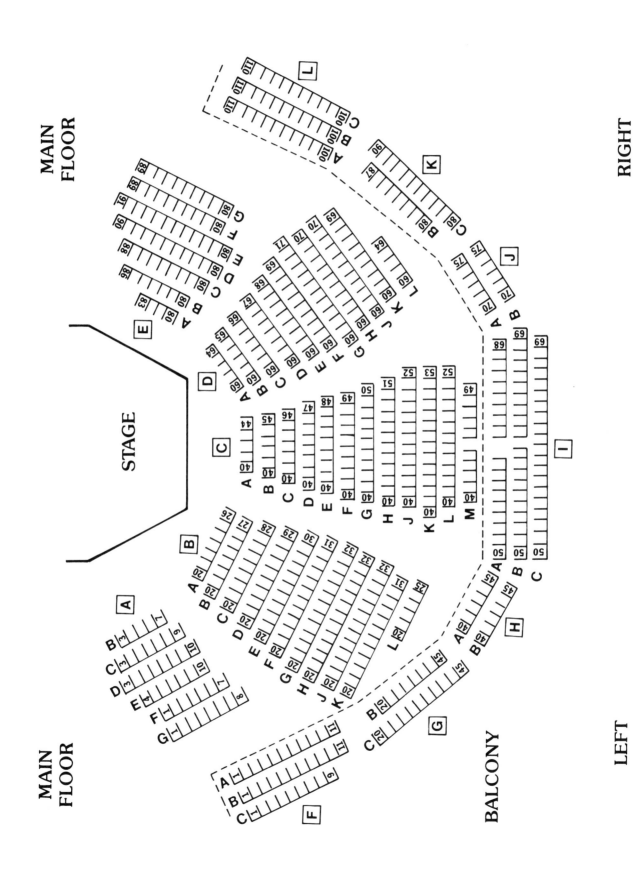

GUTHRIE THEATER

ADDRESS: 725 Vineland Place
             Minneapolis, MN 55403

TICKETS: 612-377-2224
             MN WATS 1-800-848-4912 ext. 2712

SEATING
CAPACITY: 1,441
             No seat is more than 52 feet from center stage.

SEASON: June through March.

             Special events rather than productions take the
             stage during the off-season.

HISTORY: The Guthrie Theater opened its doors on May
             7, 1963, as one of the original resident profes-
             sional theater companies. Located adjacent to
             the Walker Art Center, the Guthrie is interna-
             tionally known for the high artistic and techni-
             cal standards it maintains.

PARKING: Free street parking around the theater or you
             can choose to park in a lot for a fee.

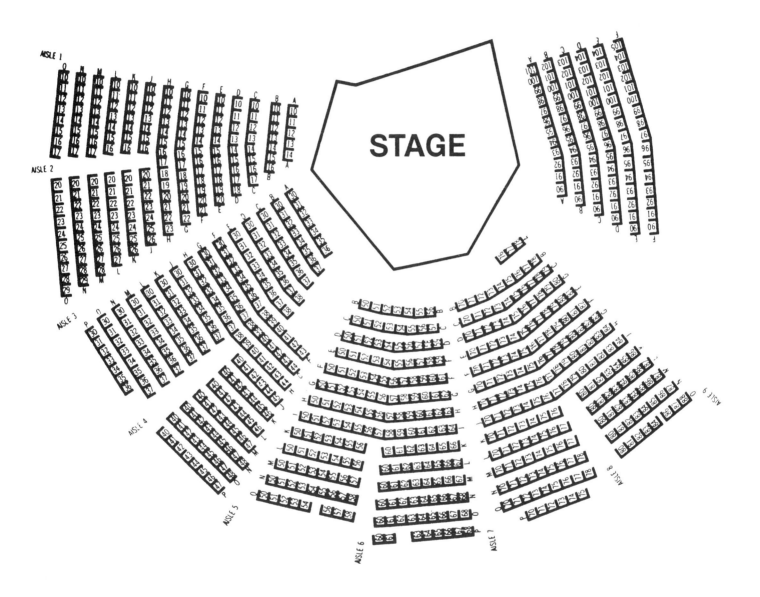

STAGE

GUTHRIE THEATER

BALCONY

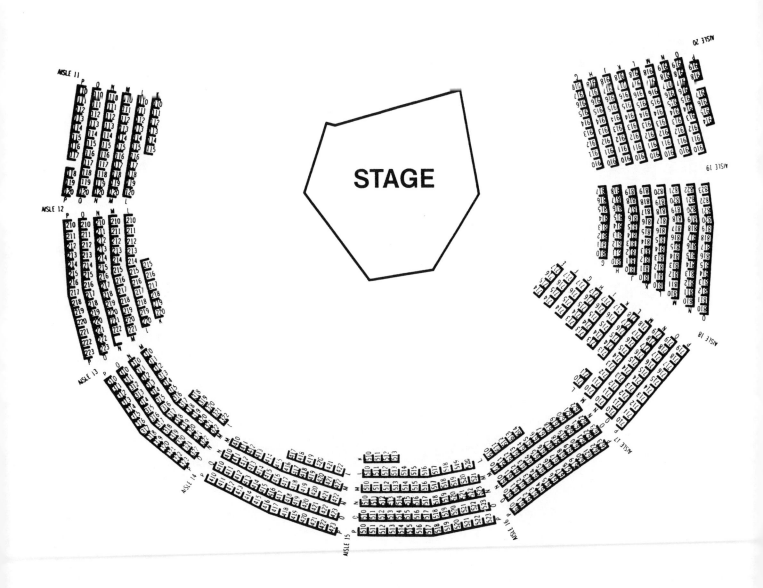

The Ordway Music Theatre (Photo courtesy of the Ordway); The Guthrie Theater (Photo courtesy of the Greater Minneapolis Convention & Visitors Association).

Theatre de la Jeune Lune (Photo courtesy of Theatre de la Jeune) Children's Theatre (Courtesy of the Minnesota Office of Tourism)

Metrodome (Photo courtesy of the Minnesota Twins)

MAYO CIVIC CENTER-ROCHESTER

ADDRESS: 30 SE Second Avenue
              Rochester, MN 55904

TICKETS: 1-800-422-2199
              507-287-2222

SEATING
CAPACITY: Arena — 5,000 to 7,200
              Auditorium — 3,000
              Theatre — 1,340

SEASON: Open throughout the year

HISTORY: The original Mayo Civic Auditorium opened in
              1939. For many years ice shows, boxing and
              pro wrestling as well as the entertainment of the
              day were held in the auditorium.

              The Mayo Civic Center Arena was opened in
              the fall of 1986. Since that time renowned
              singers, bands, theatre and orchestras have
              been performing in Rochester.

PARKING: Over 3300 parking spots are located within a
              two block radius of the Mayo Civic Center. Look
              for "Event Parking" signs or use one of the
              three downtown ramps.

ARENA

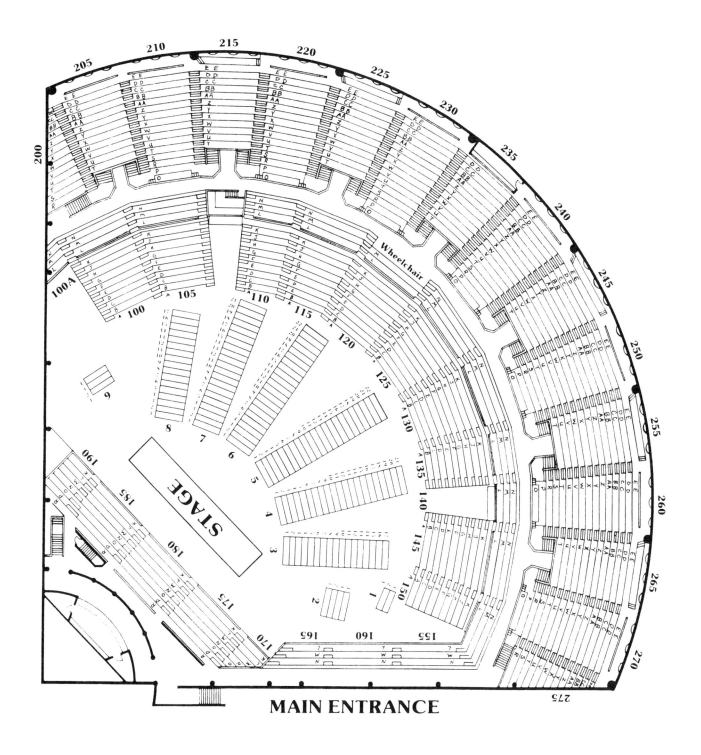

MAIN ENTRANCE

MAYO CIVIC CENTER-ROCHESTER

AUDITORIUM

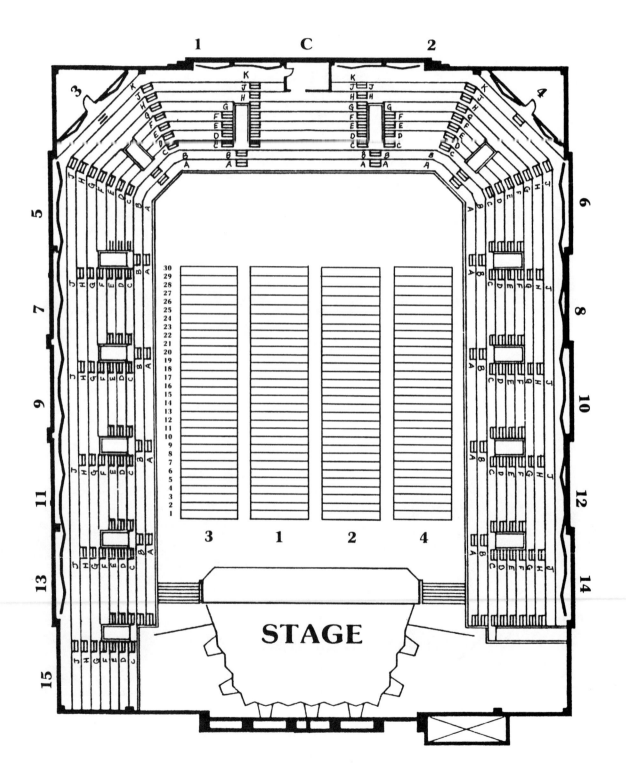

MAYO CIVIC CENTER-ROCHESTER

THEATER

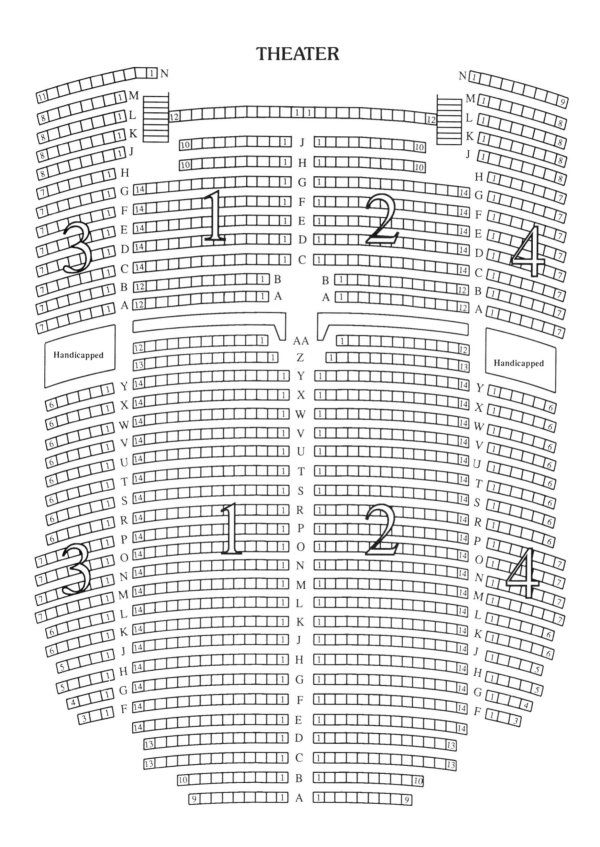

MET CENTER

ADDRESS: 7901 Cedar Avenue South
Bloomington, MN 55420

TICKETS: 612-853-9300

**SEATING
CAPACITY:** Concerts - 18,000
Sporting events - 15,650

SEASON: Open throughout the year

HISTORY: Met Center was built in 1967 by the owners of
the new North Stars hockey franchise. The team
owners rent the facility for concerts, touring ice
shows and rodeos. Other Met Center athletic
events include professional boxing, wrestling and
tennis exhibitions. The Met hosts State High
School League tournaments in basketball and
volleyball.

PARKING: A parking lot accommodating more than 6,000
vehicles surrounds the Met Center.

MET CENTER

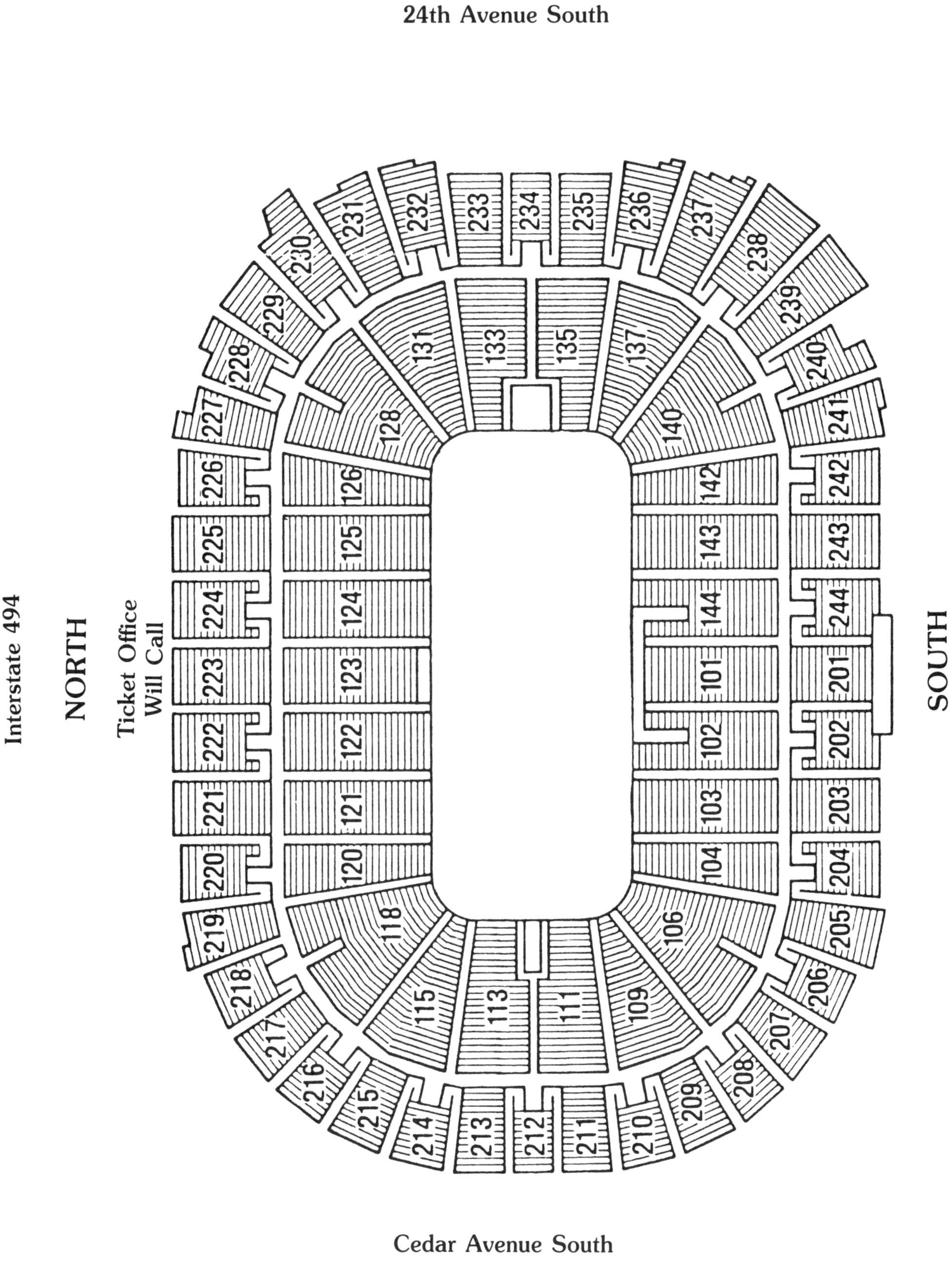

24th Avenue South
Interstate 494
NORTH
Ticket Office
Will Call
SOUTH
Cedar Avenue South
231 232 233 234 235 236 237 238 239 240 241 242 243 244 201 202 203 204 205 206 207 208 209 210 211 212 213 214 215 216 217 218 219 220 221 222 223 224 225 226 227 228 229 230
131 133 135 137 140 142 143 144 101 102 103 104 106 109 111 113 115 118 120 121 122 123 124 125 126 128

HUBERT H. HUMPHREY METRODOME

ADDRESS: 900 South Fifth Street
Minneapolis, MN 55415

TICKETS: Gophers - 612-624-8080
Twins - 612-375-1116 (charge line)
   Minnesota WATS 1-800-752-8149
Vikings - 612-333-8828

**SEATING
CAPACITY:** Baseball - 55,000
Basketball - 35,000
Football - 62,000

SEASON: This multi-purpose facility is open throughout the year.

HISTORY: Ground was broken for the Hubert H. Humphrey Metrodome on December 20, 1979 and the stadium opened April 3, 1982. It is the largest air supported multiple use stadium in the world. The metrodome is home to the Vikings, Twins and football Gophers.

The Metrodome is also a rental facility with many special events scheduled annually.

PARKING: There are 15,000 parking spaces within 6 blocks, 23,500 within 20 minutes. A fee is charged.

Shuttle bus service operates in the downtown area for all Vikings and Gophers games and most Twins games. Buses depart from marked shuttle stops one hour before and one hour following each event.

HUBERT H. HUMPHREY METRODOME

BASEBALL

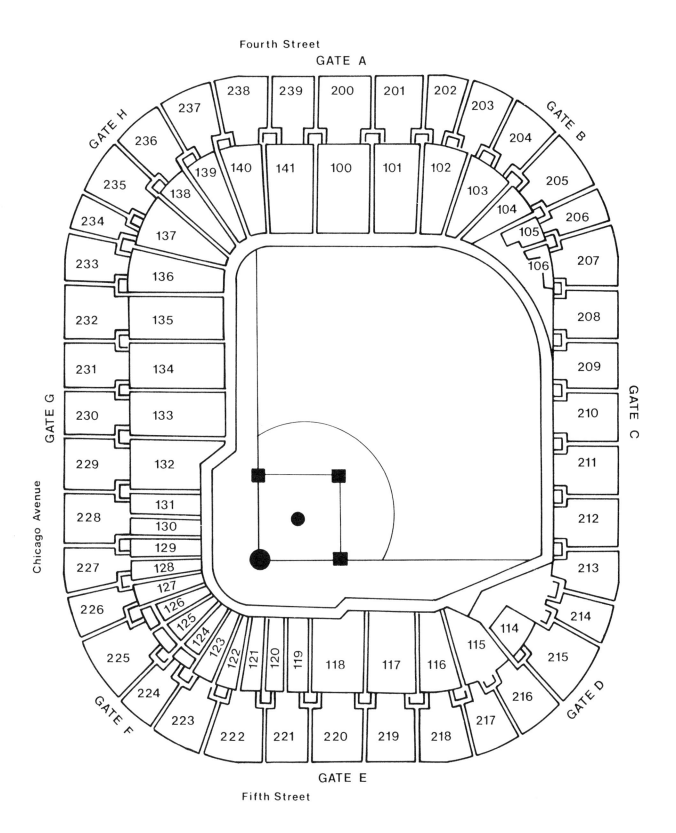

BASKETBALL

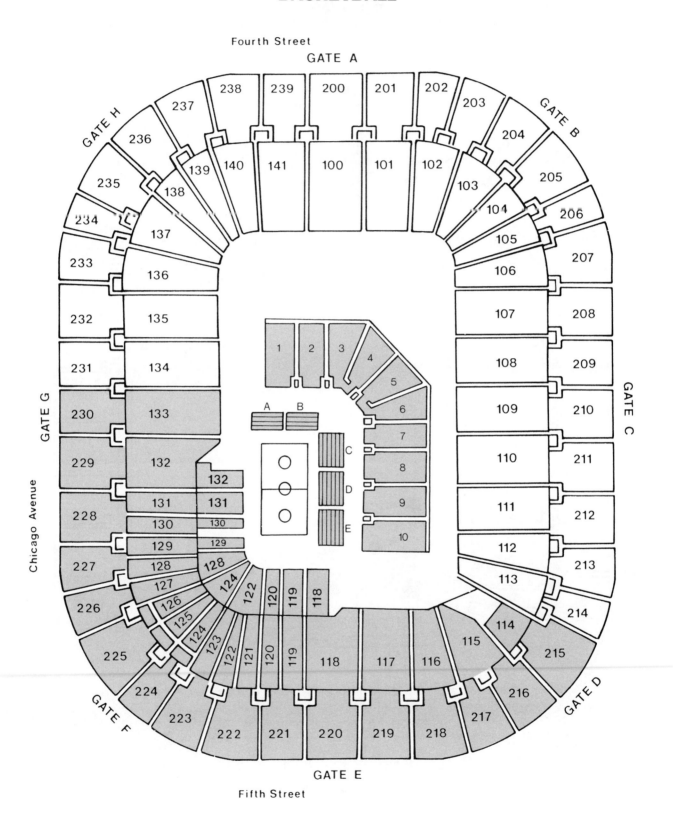

Fourth Street

GATE A

GATE H

GATE B

GATE G

GATE C

Chicago Avenue

GATE F

GATE E

GATE D

Fifth Street

HUBERT H. HUMPHREY METRODOME

FOOTBALL

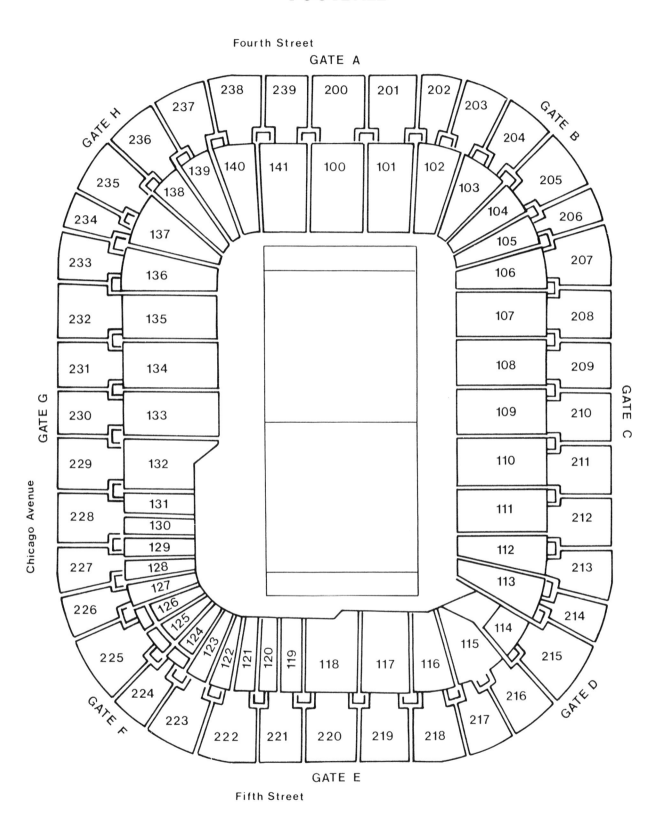

NATIONAL SPORTS CENTER

ADDRESS:	1700 105th Avenue N.E. Blaine, MN 55434	
TICKETS:	612-785-5600	
SEATING CAPACITY:	Stadium Permanent Seating	5,000
	Stadium — Temporary Seating	7,000
	Velodrome — Temporary Seating	3,000
SEASON:	Open throughout the year	

HISTORY: The National Sports Center is one of the finest athletic complexes in the nation for competition and training in cycling, soccer, track & field, weightlifting, and wrestling. Five national governing bodies have approved the center as an official training site for their sport. Construction on the National Sports Center began in the spring of 1989, and the facilities opened in January 1990. The all-wood, all-season 250 meter velodrome opened in June 1990, and it is the only velodrome like it in the United States. The National Sports Center hosts the Sons of Norway USA Cup, which is the largest youth soccer tournament in North America. The facilities are open for use by the general public through programs, leagues, facility rental, and sport specific memberships.

PARKING: A parking lot and additional parking areas accommodate more than 3,000 vehicles for National Sports Center events.

NATIONAL SPORTS CENTER

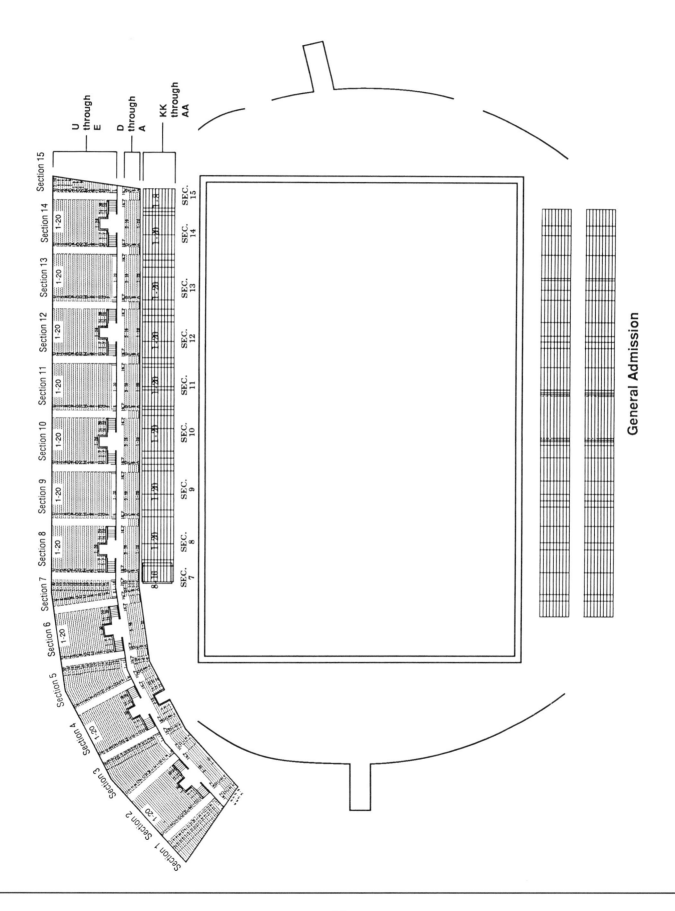

NORTHROP AUDITORIUM

ADDRESS: 84 Church Street Southeast
Minneapolis, MN 55455

TICKETS: 612-624-2345

**SEATING
CAPACITY:**   4800

SEASON.   Northrop Dance Season,
September through May.

Summer at Northrop,
Music and Dance, June to August
Many performances free and held on
Northrop Plaza.

Walker Art Center and Northrop co-sponsor
DISCOVER - Contemporary Performing Arts four
times a year.

HISTORY: Opened in 1929 with the University
Artists Course.

It was home to the Minnesota Orchestra from
1930-1973.

Host to 42 tours by the Metropolitan Opera.

Northrop Dance Season location since 1977.

PARKING: Commuter lots, garages, and free shuttle service
from Ramp B located on East River Road one
hour before performances and after until all
patrons have been served.

A curved drive accessible from Church Street is
available for handicapped patrons.

NORTHROP AUDITORIUM

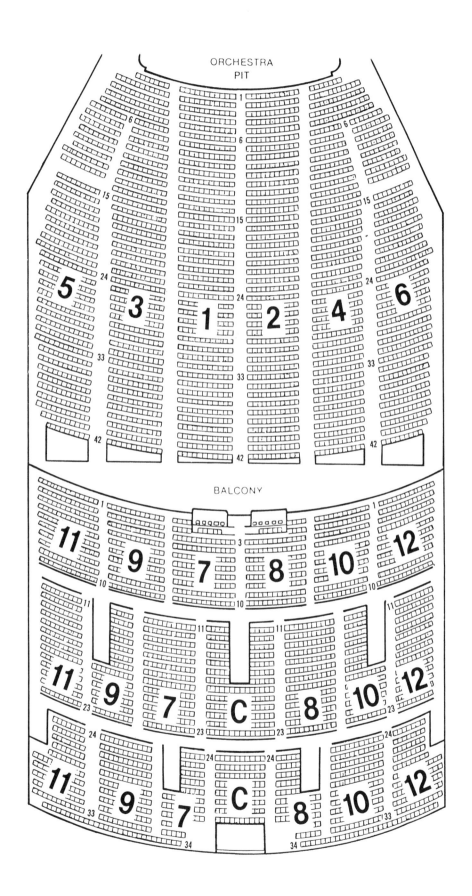

ORCHESTRA
PIT

BALCONY

OLD LOG THEATER

ADDRESS: 5175 Meadville
Excelsior, MN 55331

TICKETS: 612-474-5951

SEATING
CAPACITY: 655

SEASON: Open throughout the year
Evening performances are Wednesday through
Sunday each week. Dinner is available prior to
performance.

Matinee-luncheons on most Thursdays.

Children's shows during December. Public
performances on the first three Saturday after-
noons in December.

Off-Night Production series scheduled at vari-
ous times throughout the year on Monday and
Tuesday evenings.

HISTORY: The Old Log Theater opened its doors in 1939
and is the longest running stock theater in the
country.

In 1960, a new theater was built on 10 acres
located near Lake Minnetonka at Excelsior.

PARKING: Free parking on the grounds.

OLD LOG THEATER

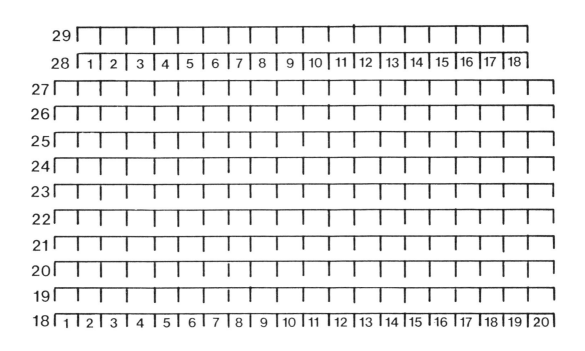

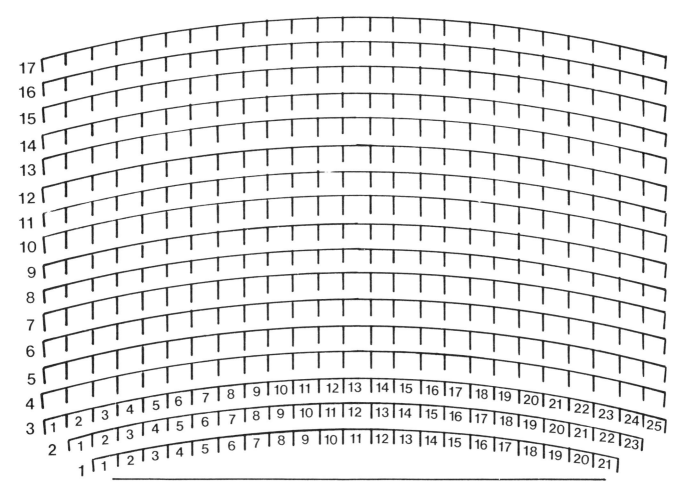

ORCHESTRA HALL

ADDRESS: 1111 Nicollet Mall
Minneapolis, MN 55403

TICKETS: 612-371-5656
Minnesota WATS 1-800-292-4141

**SEATING
CAPACITY:**   2,462

SEASON: Open throughout the year.
52 - week season includes:

24 week subscription series
Weekender Pops
Young People's Concerts
Night at the Pops
Viennese Music Festival - Sommerfest

Also:

Classical recitals featuring the world's leading artists, pops and jazz concerts and other musical events.

HISTORY: The Minnesota Orchestra was founded in 1903 and performed at the Minneapolis Exposition Hall near the Mississippi River, The Lyceum which was formerly on the Orchestra Hall site and at Northrop Auditorium from 1930-1973.

The Minnesota Orchestra first performed in Orchestra Hall on October 21, 1974.

PARKING: Event parking is available in the Orchestra Hall Ramp ($3.50), 11th Street and Marquette Avenue and in a number of surface lots within a short walk of the concert hall.

ORCHESTRA HALL

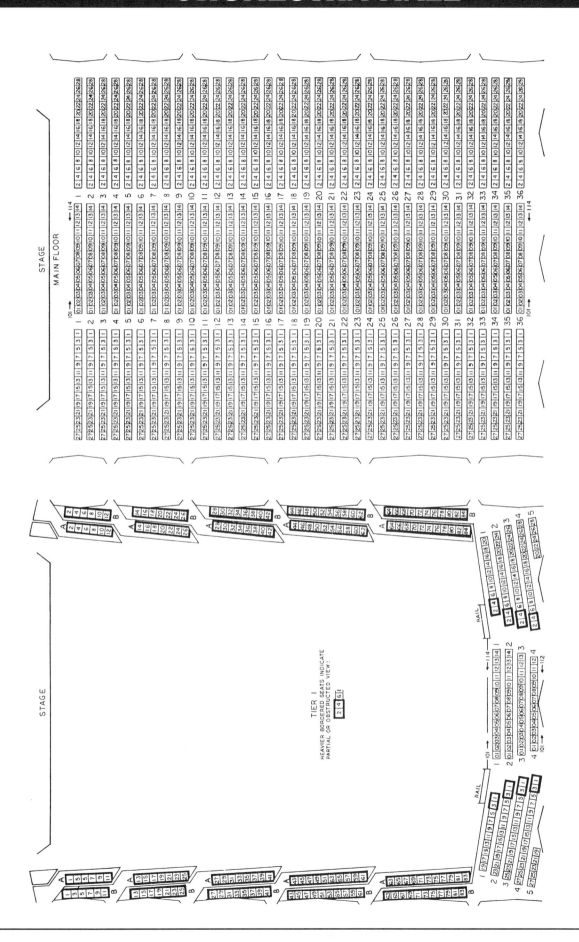

41

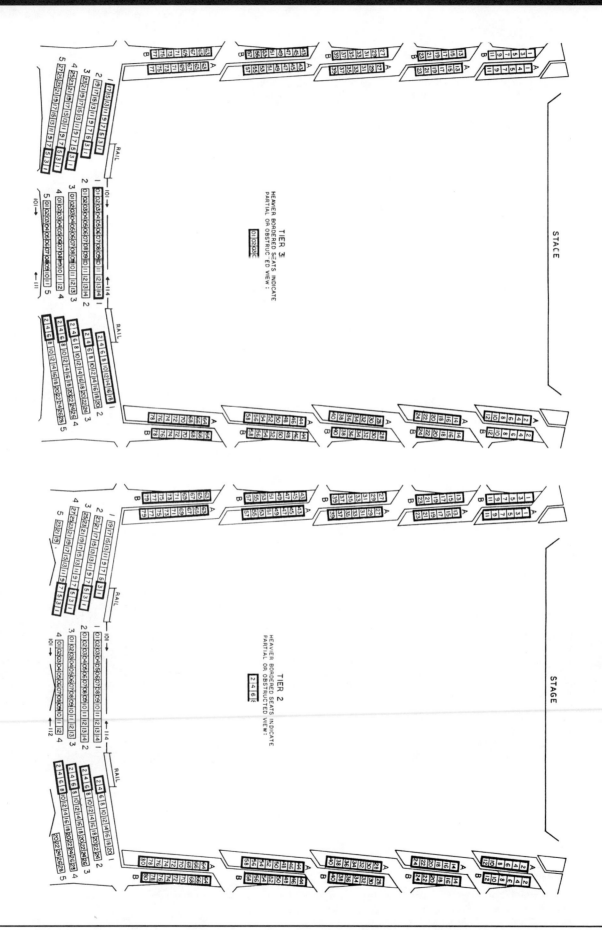

Orchestra Hall (Photo courtesy of the Greater Minneapolis Convention and Visitors Bureau)

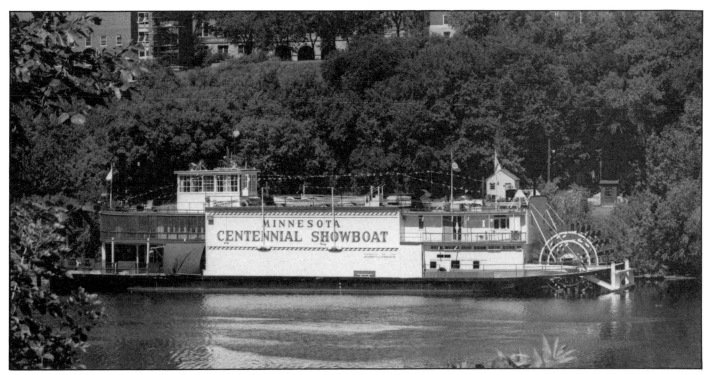

Minnesota Centennial Showboat (Photo courtesy of the Greater Minneapolis Convention and Visitors Bureau)

ORDWAY MUSIC THEATRE

ADDRESS: 345 Washington Street
              St. Paul, MN 55102

TICKETS: 612-224-4222

**SEATING
CAPACITY:**   1800

SEASON: Open throughout the year
               The Ordway accommodates orchestra, dance,
               opera and theatre.

               It is available for rent and has been used
               for benefits, and by touring companies and
               local promotors.

HISTORY: The Ordway Music Theatre became a reality on
               January 1, 1985. It is the primary performing
               home for the Saint Paul Chamber Orchestra,
               The Schubert Club and the Minnesota Opera. It
               also hosts the Minnesota Orchestra's St. Paul
               series.

PARKING: Parking lots within a four block radius include
               the St. Paul Companies lot, the Garrick Parking
               Ramp and the Amhoist and Civic Center lots.

ORDWAY MUSIC THEATRE

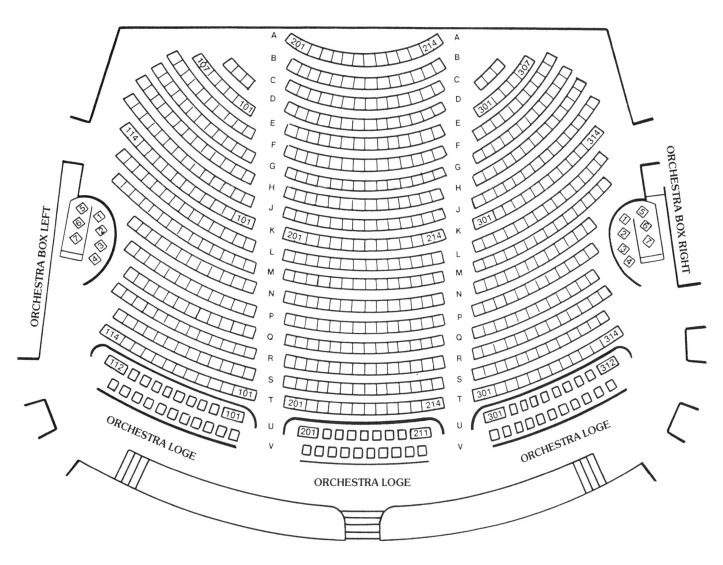

ORCHESTRA BOX LEFT

ORCHESTRA BOX RIGHT

ORCHESTRA LOGE

ORCHESTRA LOGE

ORCHESTRA LOGE

ORCHESTRA

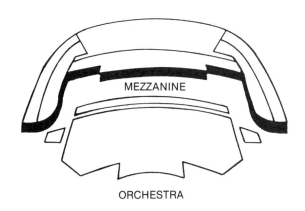

MEZZANINE

ORCHESTRA

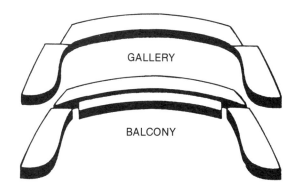

GALLERY

BALCONY

ORDWAY MUSIC THEATRE

MEZZANINE

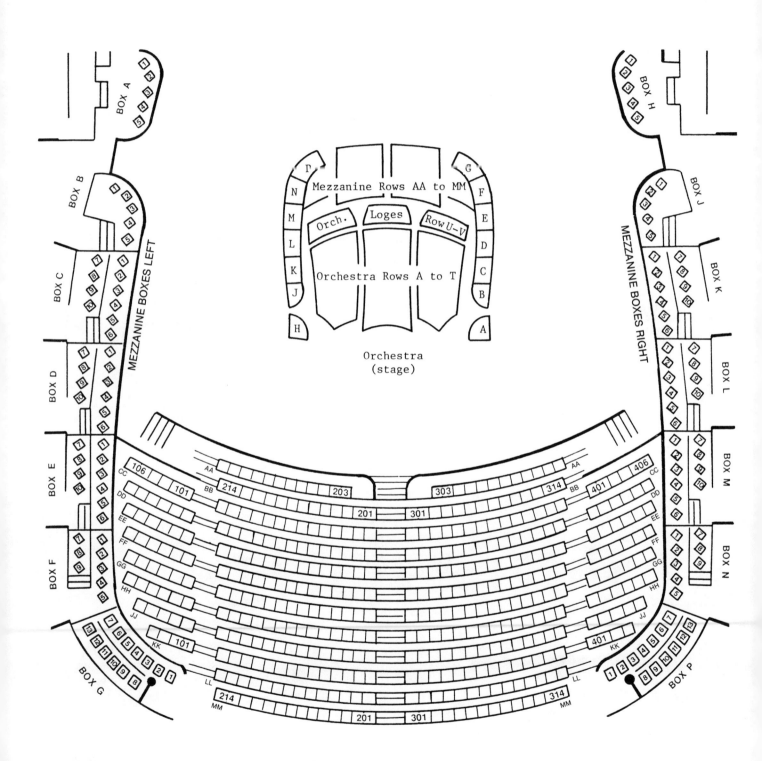

ORDWAY MUSIC THEATRE

BALCONY

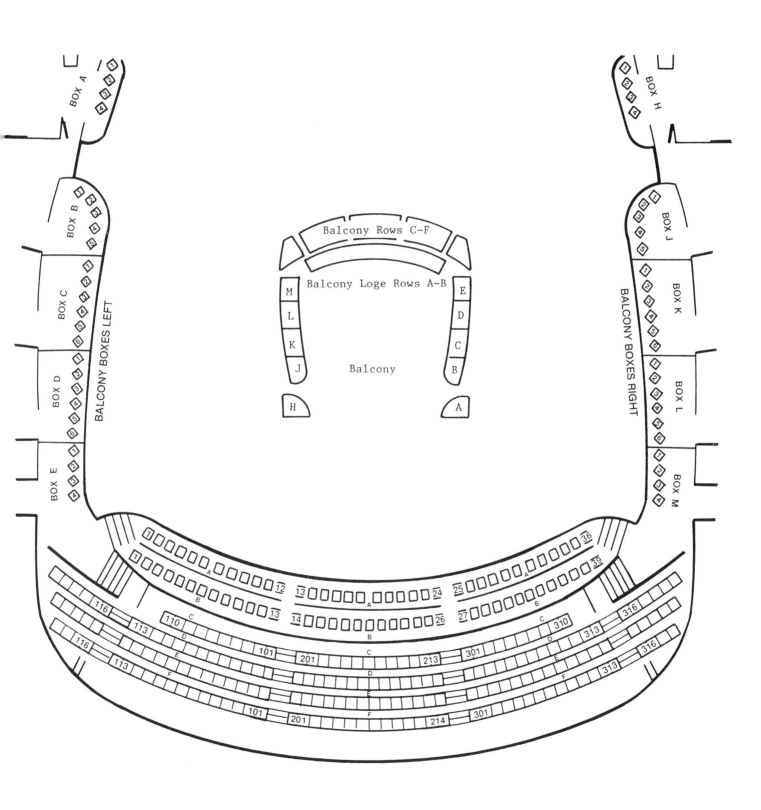

ORDWAY MUSIC THEATRE

GALLERY

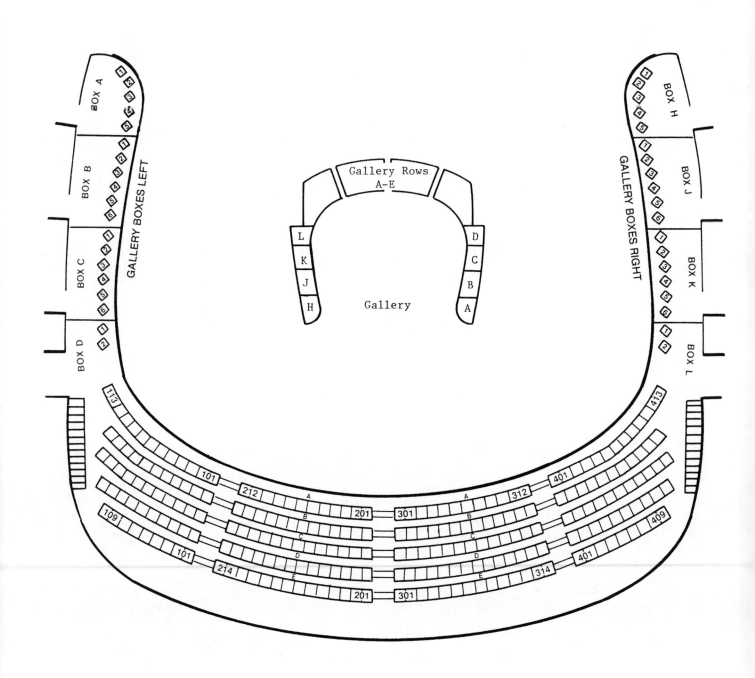

Gallery Rows
A-E

Gallery

ST. PAUL MAP

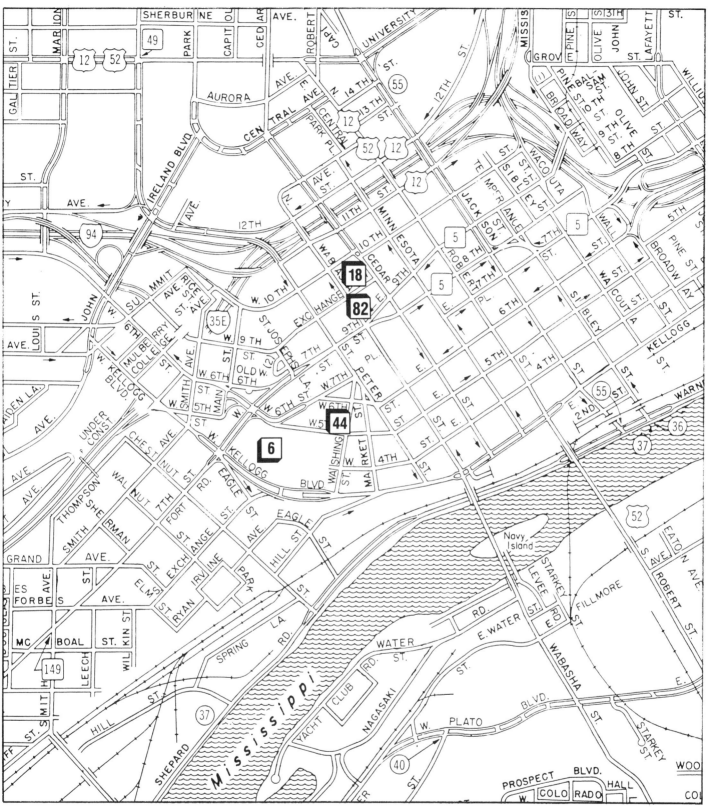

6	**CIVIC CENTER ARENA** I.A. O'Shaughnessy Plaza Seventh Street and Kellogg Blvd. St. Paul, MN 55102	18	**GREAT NORTH AMERICAN HISTORY THEATRE** Minnesota Science Museum 30 E. 10th Street St. Paul, MN 55101	82	**WORLD THEATER** 10 East Exchange Street St. Paul, MN 55101
		44	**ORDWAY MUSIC THEATRE** 345 Washington Street St. Paul, MN 55102		

ORPHEUM THEATRE

ADDRESS: 910 Hennepin Avenue
                      Minneapolis, MN 55403

TICKETS: 612-339-7007   Orpheum Box Office
                      612-989-5151   Ticketmaster

SEATING
CAPACITY: 2,741

SEASON: Open throughout the year

HISTORY: The Orpheum Theatre opened its doors on October 16, 1921 and quickly became the major theatre in Minneapolis for the prestigious Orpheum circuit, one of the two major vaudeville circuits in the nation.

Talking motion pictures replaced vaudeville in the 1930's, with live orchestras becoming the main attraction from 1937 through the 40's. Broadway touring productions began in 1959 and continue today.

Previous owners include Ted Mann and Bob Dylan who purchased it in 1978. In July, 1988, the Minneapolis Community Development Agency acquired the facility. Many improvements have been made to permit a wide variety of uses including rental for private use.

PARKING: Ample ramp, surface and street parking in the immediate area.

ORPHEUM THEATRE

MAIN FLOOR

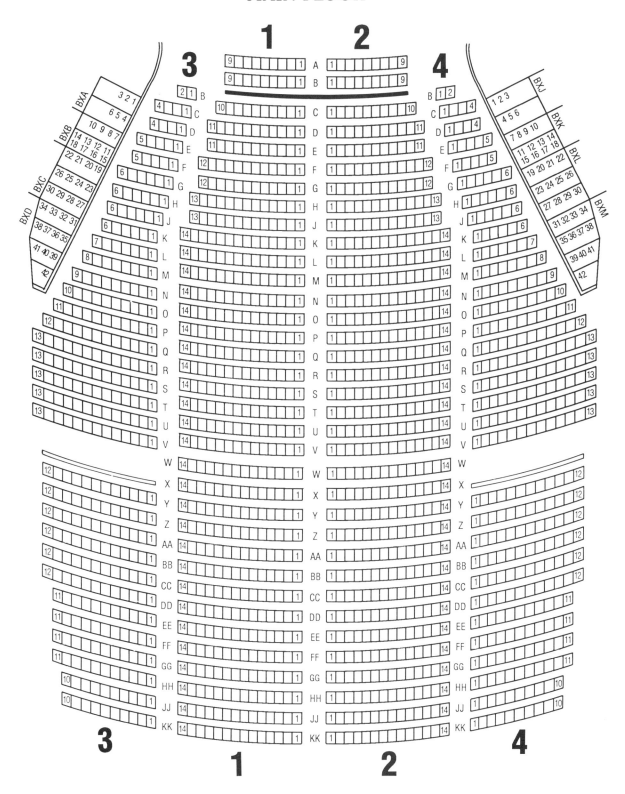

ORPHEUM THEATRE

BALCONY

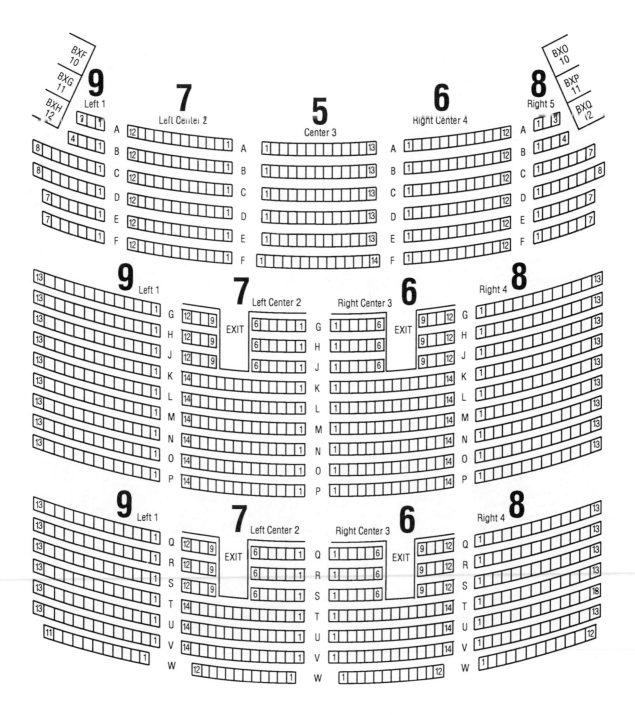

METROPOLITAN AREA MAP

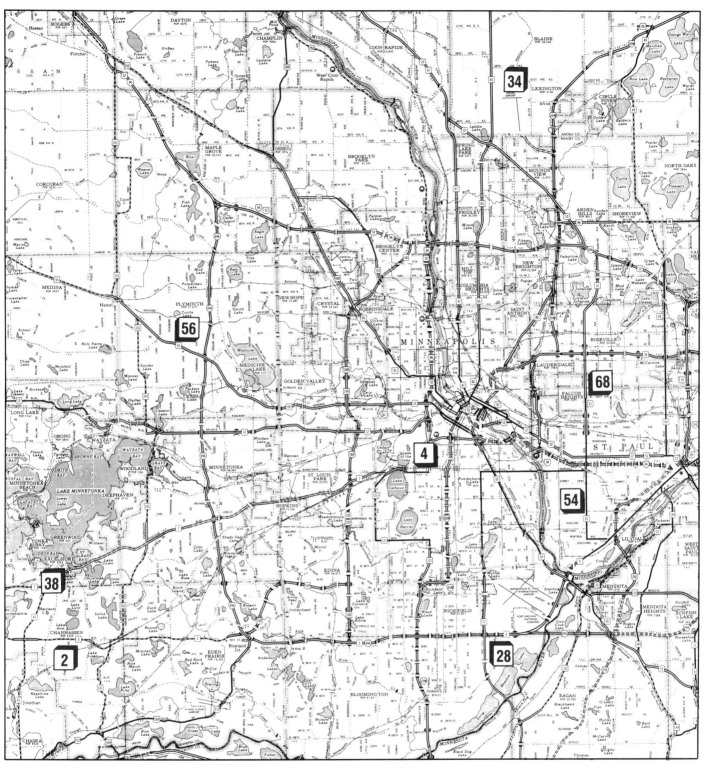

2   CHANHASSEN DINNER THEATRES
501 West 78th St.
Chanhassen, MN 56317

4   CHILDREN'S THEATRE
2400 Third Avenue South
Minneapolis, MN 55404

28   MET CENTER
7901 Cedar Avenue South
Bloomington, MN 55420

34   NATIONAL SPORTS CENTER
1700 105th Avenue NE
Blaine, MN 55434

38   OLD LOG THEATER
5175 Meadville
Excelsior, MN 55331

54   O'SHAUGHNESSY AUDITORIUM
2004 Randolph Avenue
College of St. Catherine
St. Paul, MN 55116

56   PLYMOUTH PLAYHOUSE
I-494 and Highway 55 (Quality Inn)
2705 Annapolis Lane
Plymouth, MN 55441

68   STATE FAIR GRANDSTAND
North Snelling Avenue
St. Paul, MN 55108

O'SHAUGHNESSEY AUDITORIUM

ADDRESS: 2004 Randolph Avenue
College of St. Catherine
St. Paul, MN 55116

TICKETS: 612-690-6700

**SEATING
CAPACITY:**   1800

SEASON: Open throughout the year for rental

HISTORY: Built in 1972, O'Shaughnessey is primarily a rental facility on the College of St. Catherine. It is the former home stage for the St. Paul Chamber Orchestra and the Minnesota Orchestra's St. Paul concerts.

PARKING: Parking is free on the campus with no permit required after 5:00 p.m.

O'SHAUGHNESSEY AUDITORIUM

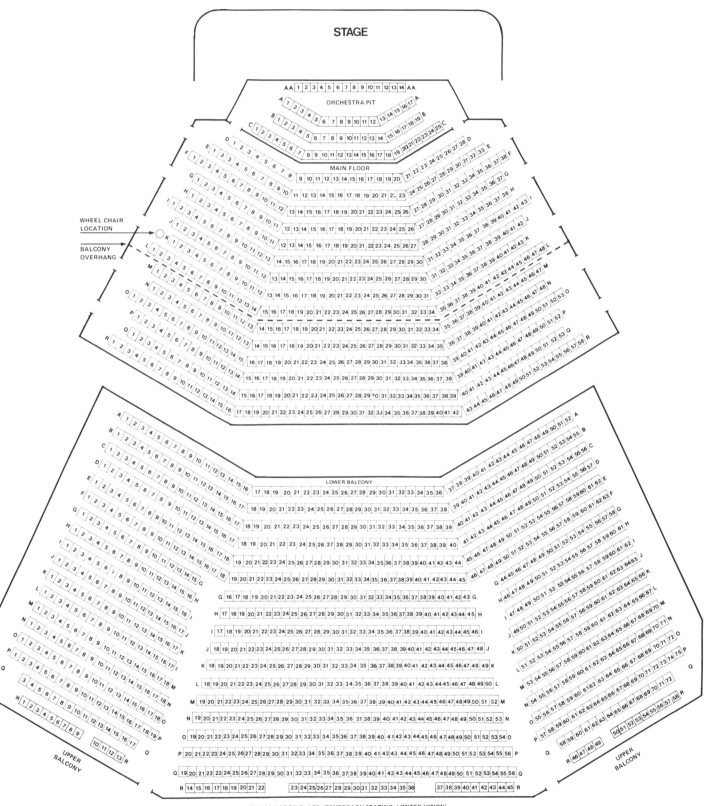

WHEEL CHAIR LOCATION

BALCONY OVERHANG

STAGE

ORCHESTRA PIT

MAIN FLOOR

LOWER BALCONY

UPPER BALCONY

UPPER BALCONY

(BALCONY ROW R, 1-58: TEMPORARY SEATING, LIMITED VISION)

55

PLYMOUTH PLAYHOUSE

ADDRESS: Plymouth Place Hotel at I-494 & Hwy 55
                    2705 Annapolis Lane
                    Plymouth, MN 55441

TICKETS: 612-553-1600

SEATING
CAPACITY: 200

HISTORY: Opened in 1976, this professional theatre has
                    won awards for choreography, direction, and
                    best production.

PARKING: Free parking in motel lot.

PLYMOUTH PLAYHOUSE

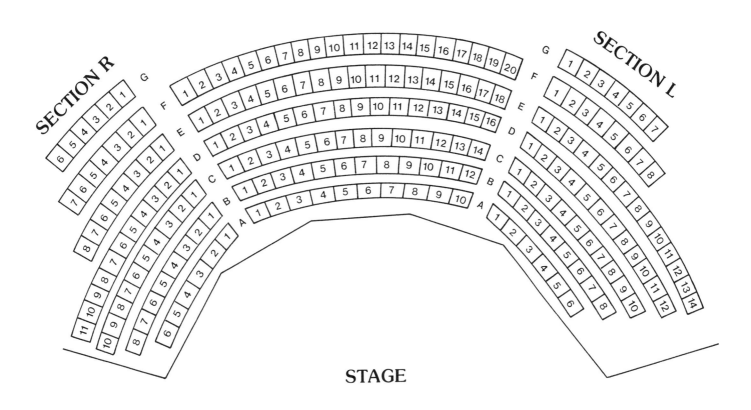

SECTION R

SECTION L

STAGE

RARIG CENTER UNIVERSITY THEATRES

ADDRESS: 330 South 21st Avenue
University of Minnesota
Minneapolis, MN 55455

TICKETS: 612-625-4001

**SEATING
CAPACITY:** Arena 206
Stoll Thrust 486
Whiting Proscenium 459

SEASON: Regular season runs during the school year,
October through May.

During the summer, performances on the
Minnesota Centennial Showboat. Typically,
mid-June to early September.

HISTORY: Rarig Center, the building that houses the four
theatres, was built in 1972.

The Arena, Thrust and Proscenium Theatres are
all reserved seating. The fourth stage, the Experi-
mental or Laboratory Theatre, is an open space
where up to 150 spectators can view productions.

The Centennial Showboat is general admission.

PARKING: University parking - nearby ramp.

RARIG CENTER UNIVERSITY THEATRES

ARENA
THEATRE

Second Floor

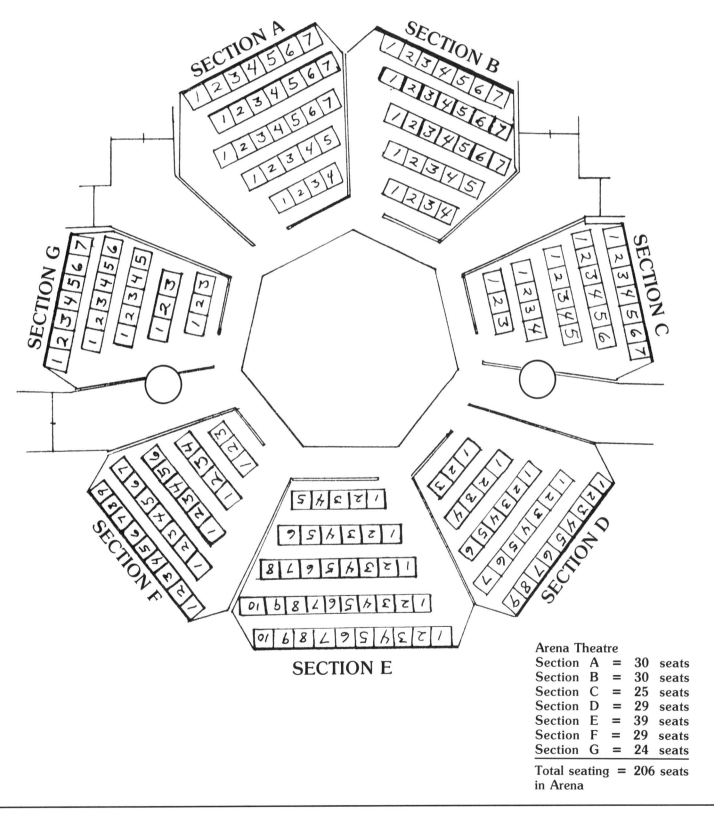

Arena Theatre
Section A = 30 seats
Section B = 30 seats
Section C = 25 seats
Section D = 29 seats
Section E = 39 seats
Section F = 29 seats
Section G = 24 seats

Total seating = 206 seats
in Arena

STOLL THRUST
THEATRE

First Floor

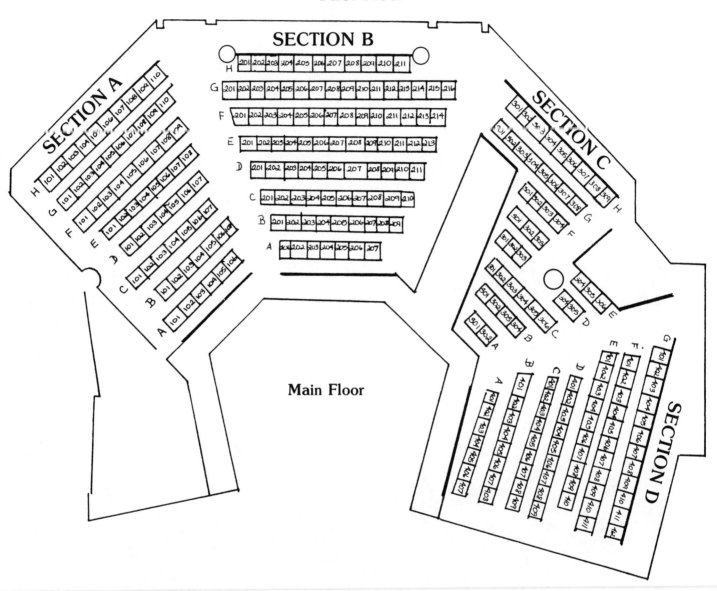

Main Floor

Section A = 63 seats
Section B = 91 seats
Section C = 44 seats
Section D = 66 seats

Total main floor seats = 264
Total Thrust seating = 486

STOLL THRUST
THEATRE

Second Floor

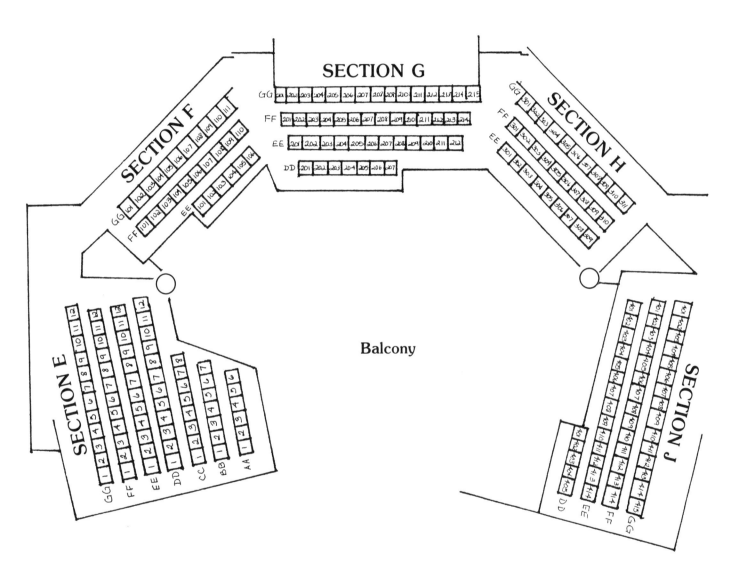

Balcony

Total balcony seating = 222
Total Thrust seating = 486

Section E = 69 seats
Section F = 27 seats
Section G = 48 seats
Section H = 30 seats
Section J = 48 seats

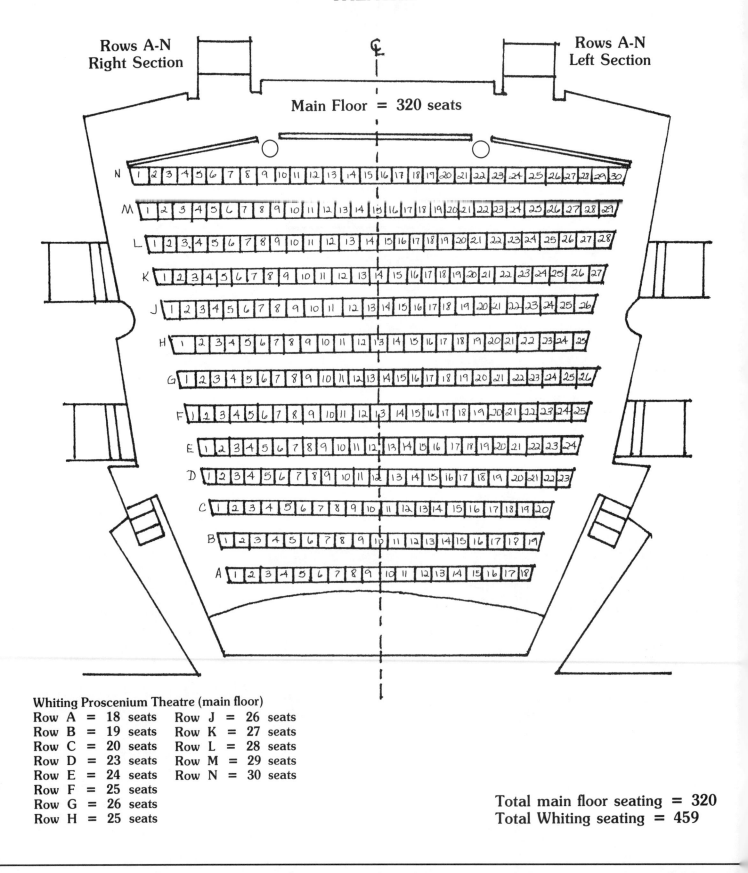

WHITING PROSCENIUM THEATRE

Rows A-N Right Section

Rows A-N Left Section

Main Floor = 320 seats

Whiting Proscenium Theatre (main floor)

Row A	=	18 seats	Row J = 26 seats
Row B	=	19 seats	Row K = 27 seats
Row C	=	20 seats	Row L = 28 seats
Row D	=	23 seats	Row M = 29 seats
Row E	=	24 seats	Row N = 30 seats
Row F	=	25 seats	
Row G	=	26 seats	
Row H	=	25 seats	

Total main floor seating = 320
Total Whiting seating = 459

RARIG CENTER UNIVERSITY THEATRES

WHITING PROSCENIUM THEATRE

Second Floor

Rows AA-FF
Right Section

Rows AA-GG
Left Section

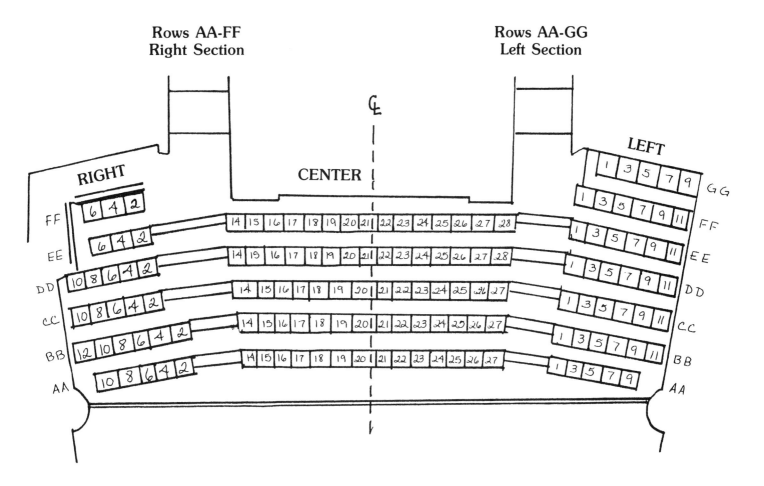

Whiting Proscenium Theatre (balcony)
Row AA = 24 seats
Row BB = 26 seats
Row CC = 25 seats
Row DD = 26 seats
Row EE = 24 seats
Row FF = 9 seats
Row GG = 5 seats

Total balcony seating = 139
Total Whiting seating = 459

ADDRESS: P.O. Box 34
             Third Street at East Avenue
             Red Wing, MN 55066

TICKETS: 612-388-2806
             Box office hours:
             Monday — Saturday 12:00-5:00 P.M.
             Two hours prior to scheduled performances with
             the exception of high school events and films.

SEATING
CAPACITY: 471

SEASON: Open throughout the year. Season brochures
             are available in late May of each year.

HISTORY: The first municipal theatre in the nation, this
             turn-of-the-century theatre was described as a
             jewel box in 1904. The Sheldon was restored to
             its original elegance in 1988.

PARKING: Free parking is available behind the theatre in a
             municipal ramp.

FIRST FLOOR

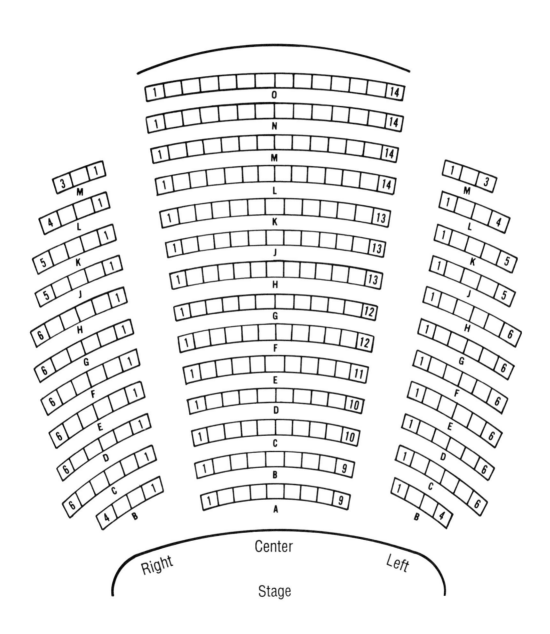

BALCONY

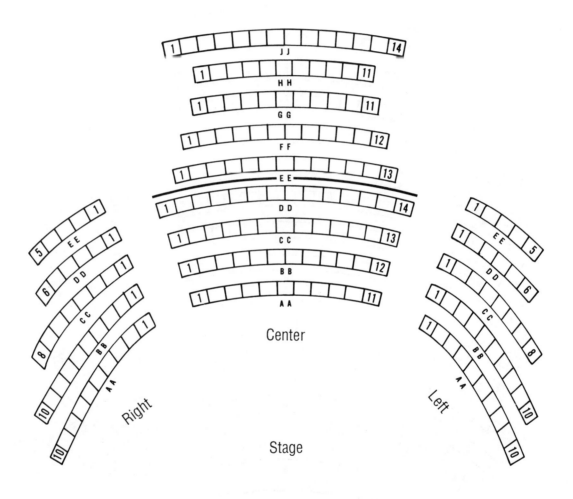

Center

Right

Left

Stage

OUTSTATE MAPS

RED WING

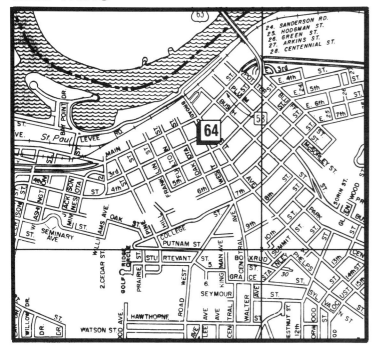

ROCHESTER

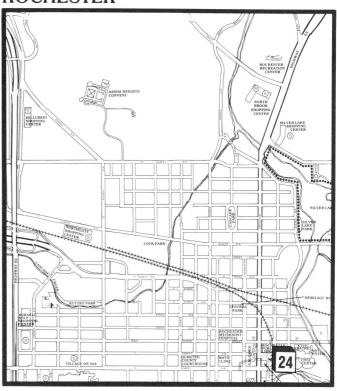

DULUTH

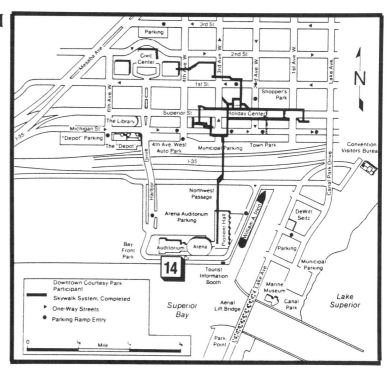

14   DULUTH ENTERTAINMENT CONVENTION CENTER
      350 Harbor Drive
      Duluth, MN 55802

24   MAYO CIVIC CENTER-ROCHESTER
      30 SE Second Avenue
      Rochester, MN 55904

64   T.B. SHELDON AUDITORIUM THEATRE
      P.O. Box 34
      Third Street at East Avenue
      Red Wing, MN 55066

STATE FAIR GRANDSTAND

ADDRESS: State Fairgrounds
North Snelling Avenue
St. Paul, MN 55108

TICKETS: 612-642-2262

**SEATING
CAPACITY:**   Reserved 11,936
General admission bleachers 9,000
Total 20,936

SEASON: Eleven evening concerts and one day of
auto racing.

HISTORY: Built in 1909.

Available for rent - infield for swap meets,
car shows, etc.

PARKING: Fairgrounds parking is free. However, there is an
admission charge to the grounds during the fair.

STATE FAIR GRANDSTAND

ROOF ABOVE

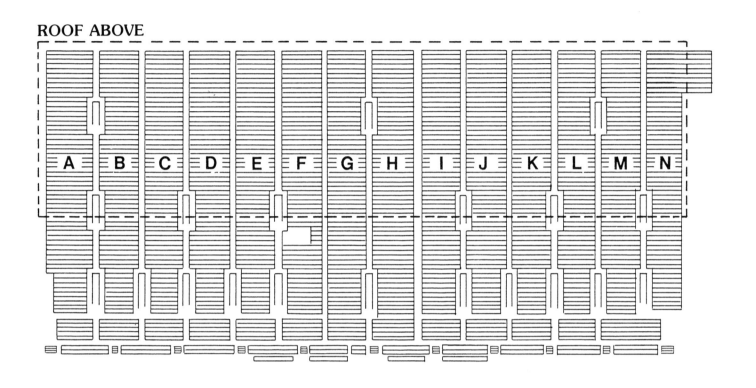

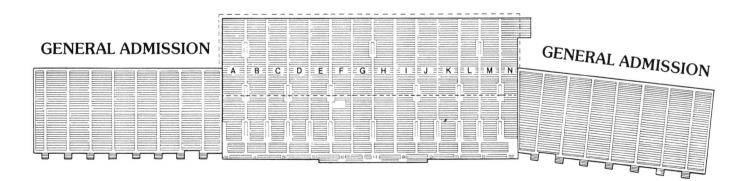

GENERAL ADMISSION

GENERAL ADMISSION

STATE THEATRE

ADDRESS: 807 Hennepin Avenue
Minneapolis, Minnesota 55403

TICKETS: 612-339-7007   Box Office
612-989-5151   Ticketmaster

SEATING
CAPACITY: Auditorium   2,176

SEASON: Open throughout the year. The State Theatre
accommodates musicals, operas, popular concerts, first-run Broadway shows, films and a
wide variety of other performing arts events.
Theatre rental is also available.

HISTORY: The State Theatre opened on February 5,1921
as a presentation house for talkies, vaudeville
acts, and later concerts, ballet and touring
Broadway shows.

In 1958, the theatre became the city's prime
stage for Broadway shows, and has since closed
and re-opened several times.

The Minneapolis Community Development
Agency purchased the theatre and completed
an $8.8 million renovation in 1991. Much of the
original ornamentation has been restored including crystal chandeliers, molded plaster
cherubs, and painted wall murals.

The theatre is now the centerpiece of LaSalle
Plaza.

PARKING: A 3,000 stall municipal parking garage, connected to LaSalle Plaza is located one and one-
half blocks away. LaSalle Plaza provides below-
grade parking within the complex for 330 cars.
An additional 2,200 spaces are available within
a one-block radius.

STATE THEATRE

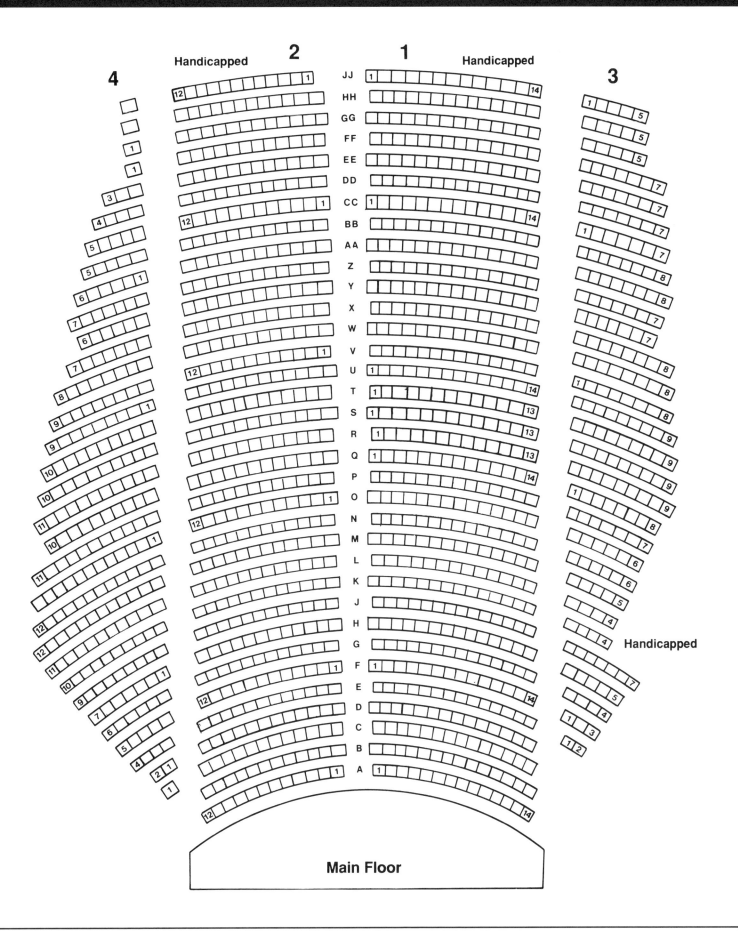

Main Floor

71

STATE THEATRE

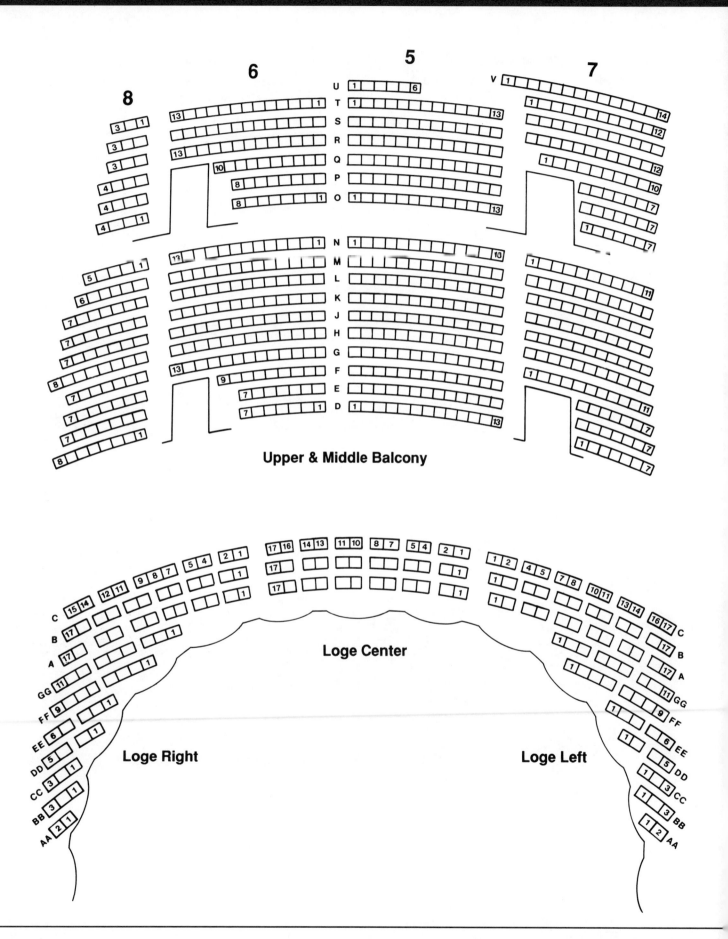

Upper & Middle Balcony

Loge Center

Loge Right

Loge Left

Restored State Theatre, Proscenium Arch

TARGET CENTER

ADDRESS: 600 1st Avenue North
                Minneapolis, MN 55403

TICKETS: 612-337-3865

SEATING
CAPACITY: Timberwolves Arena 18,200

SEASON: The NBA season is October through April with
                forty-one regular home season games.

                Timberwolves Arena will be open for other
                events throughout the year.

HISTORY: The NBA franchise was awarded to Minnesota
                on April 22, 1987. Groundbreaking ceremonies
                for the new Timberwolves Arena were held July
                12, 1988.

PARKING: More than 10,000 parking spaces circle the
                arena in a three block area. Two new parking
                garages across the street will be connected by a
                skyway.

TARGET CENTER

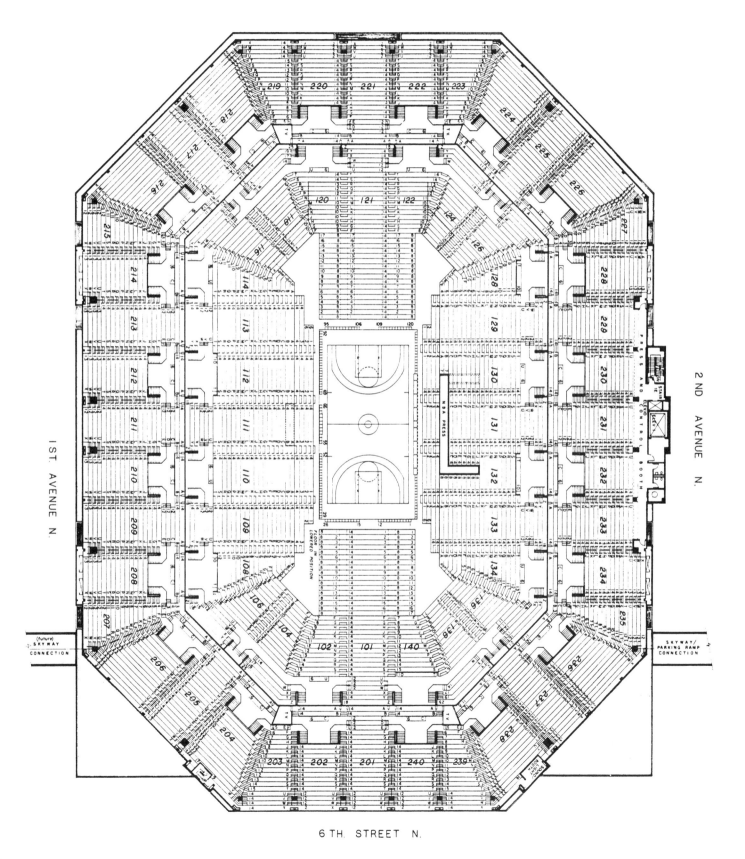

7 TH. STREET N.

6 TH. STREET N.

1 ST. AVENUE N.

2 ND AVENUE N.

THEATRE IN THE ROUND

ADDRESS: 245 Cedar Avenue
Minneapolis, MN 55454

TICKETS: 612-333-3010

**SEATING
CAPACITY:**   261
No seat is more than 30 feet from center stage.

SEASON: Open throughout the year
10 shows, eight during the regular season of
September to June and two summer productions.

HISTORY: Theatre in the Round has had three homes:
Benton Hall of the YWCA (1953-63)
1308 Stevens Avenue (1963-69)
245 Cedar Avenue (1969 to present)

Founded in 1952, TRP is the oldest community
theatre in the Twin Cities and has won a number
of awards.

PARKING: Municipal ramp near Grandma's Restaurant and
the Holiday Inn.

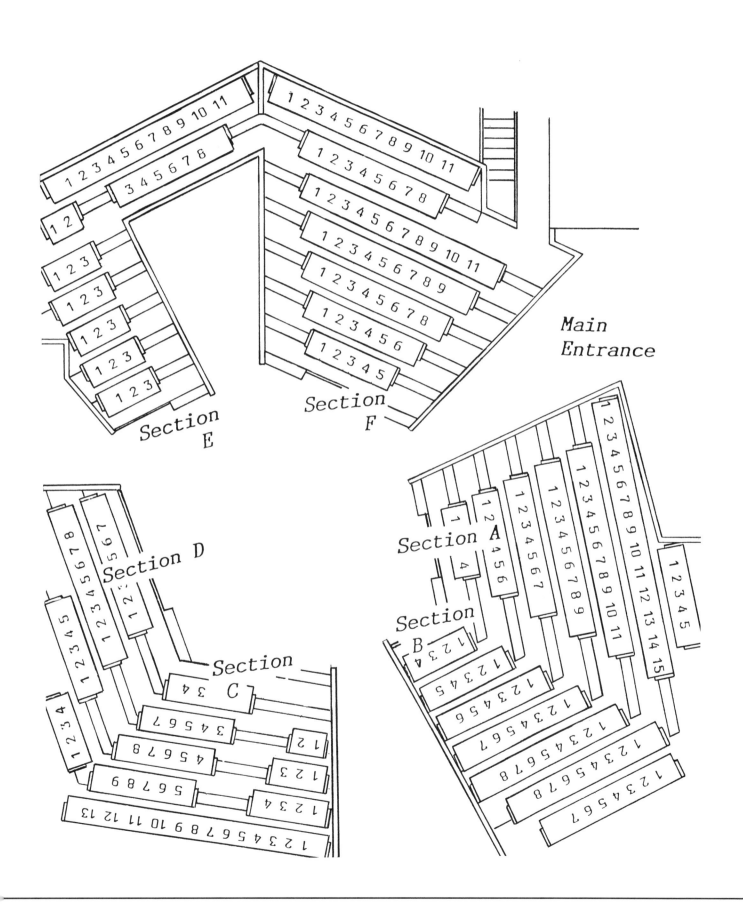

Main
Entrance

Section
E

Section
F

Section D

Section
C

Section A

Section
B

WILLIAMS ARENA

ADDRESS: 1901 University Avenue Southeast
University of Minnesota Campus
Minneapolis, MN 55455

TICKETS: 612-624-8080
(for all University athletic events)

**SEATING
CAPACITY:** Williams Arena, basketball, 16,462
Mariucci Arena, hockey, 7,625

SEASON: Men's basketball, November through March.
Hockey, October through April.

Williams Arena is used for women's sports
including basketball, volleyball and gymnastics.

This facility is available for rent to high schools.

HISTORY: Built in 1928.

WILLIAMS ARENA

BASKETBALL

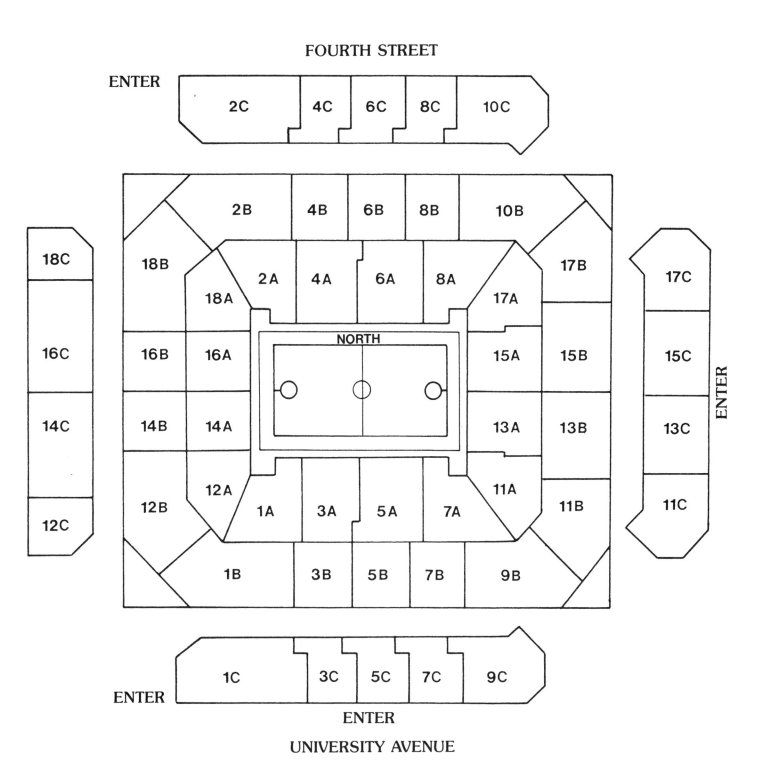

FOURTH STREET

ENTER

ENTER

ENTER

UNIVERSITY AVENUE

MARIUCCI ARENA

HOCKEY

FOURTH STREET

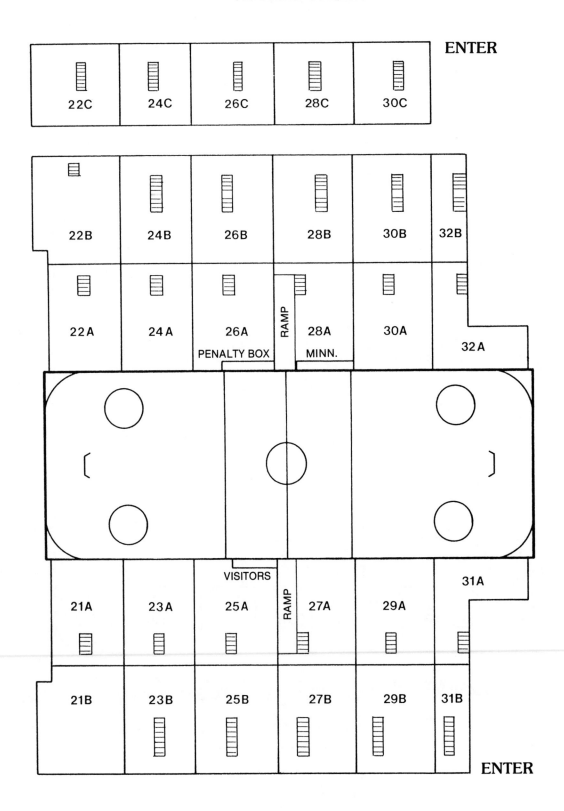

ENTER

22C 24C 26C 28C 30C

22B 24B 26B 28B 30B 32B

22A 24A 26A RAMP 28A 30A 32A

PENALTY BOX MINN.

VISITORS

21A 23A 25A RAMP 27A 29A 31A

21B 23B 25B 27B 29B 31B

ENTER

UNIVERSITY AVENUE

MINNEAPOLIS MAP

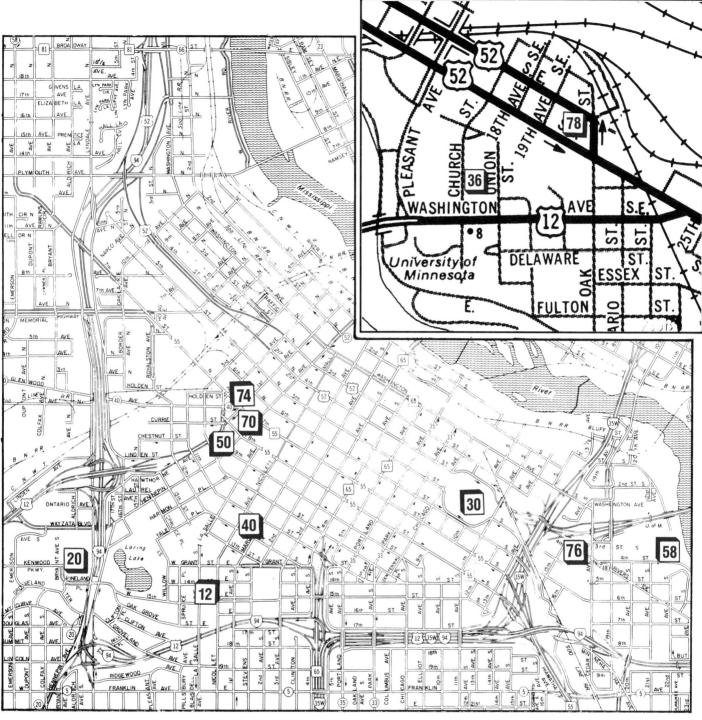

12	CRICKET THEATRE 1407 Nicollet Avenue Minneapolis, MN 55403	40	ORCHESTRA HALL 111 Nicollet Mall Minneapolis, MN 55403	74	TARGET CENTER 600 1st Avenue North Minneapolis, MN 55403
20	GUTHRIE THEATER 725 Vineland Place Minneapolis, MN 55403	50	ORPHEUM THEATRE 910 Hennepin Avenue Minneapolis, MN 55403	76	THEATRE IN THE ROUND 245 Cedar Avenue Minneapolis, MN 55454
30	METRODOME 900 South Fifth Street Minneapolis, MN 55415	58	RARIG CENTER University of Minnesota 330 South 21st Avenue Minneapolis, MN 55455	78	WILLIAMS ARENA Mariucci Arena 1901 University Avenue Southeast University of Minnesota Campus Minneapolis, MN 55455
36	NORTHRUP MEMORIAL AUDITORIUM 84 Church Street Southeast Minneapolis, MN 55455	70	STATE THEATRE 806 Hennepin Avenue Minneapolis, MN 55403		

WORLD THEATER

ADDRESS: 10 East Exchange Street
                 St. Paul, MN 55101

TICKETS: 612-298-1300
                 Box Office and Gift Shop hours:
                    10:00 AM - 5:30 PM Monday - Saturday
                    Three hours prior to scheduled performances
                    on Sunday.

**SEATING
CAPACITY:**   916
                 No seat is more than 87 feet from center stage in
                 this two-balcony hall.

SEASON: Open throughout the year
                 It schedules classical, jazz, folk, country and pop
                 music events, as well as film screenings and
                 theatrical productions.

HISTORY: Opened as the Sam S. Shubert Theater in 1910,
                 the name was changed to the World Theater in
                 1933. Noted for its rich simplicity, it was
                 restored to the original elegance in 1986.

                 The World Theater was home to A PRAIRIE
                 HOME COMPANION™ for 10 years, and its
                 restoration was initiated by Garrison Keillor's
                 'Save the World' benefit.

PARKING: One of the most convenient theaters to reach,
                 the Seventh Street Municipal Ramp offers more
                 than 500 spaces located directly behind the
                 theater between Cedar and Wabasha Streets.

MAIN FLOOR

OUTER LOBBY

INNER LOBBY

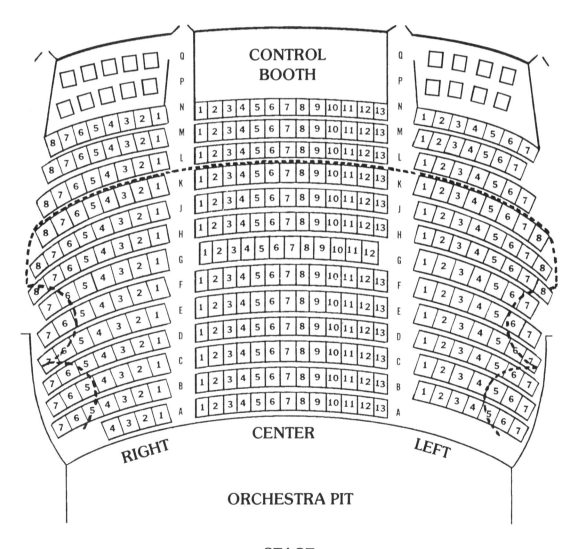

CONTROL BOOTH

CENTER

RIGHT

LEFT

ORCHESTRA PIT

STAGE

WORLD THEATER

FIRST BALCONY

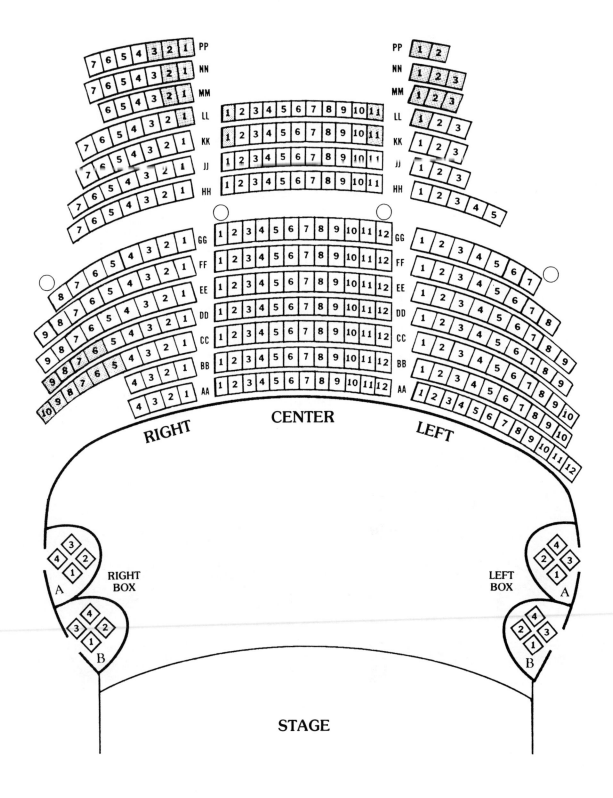

WORLD THEATER

SECOND BALCONY

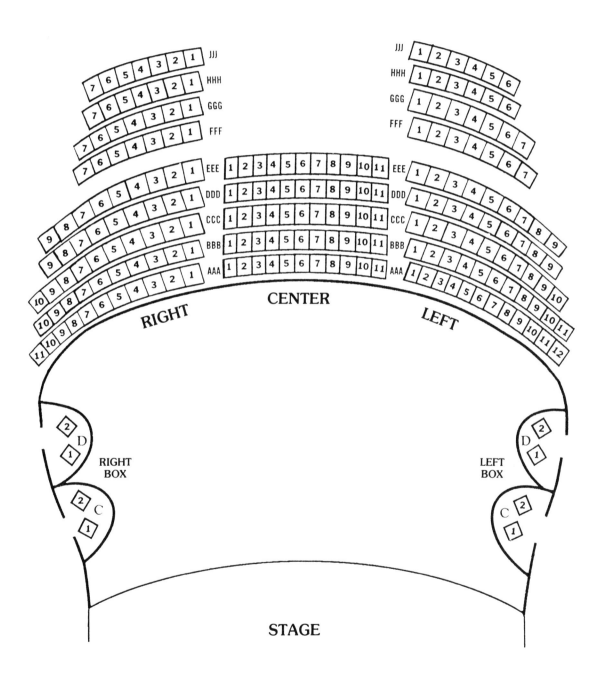

GENERAL ADMISSION

CAMPUS LIVE THEATER
309 Oak St. S.E.
Minneapolis, MN 55414
Tickets 612-378-3770

CHILDS PLAY THEATRE CO.
Eisenhower Community Center
Highway 7 and 12th Ave.
Hopkins, MN 55343
Tickets 612-925-5250

**DUDLEY RIGGS BRAVE
NEW WORKSHOP**
Instantaneous Theatre,
    Improvisational
2605 Hennepin Ave. S.
Minneapolis, MN 55408
Tickets 612-332-6620

**GILBERT AND SULLIVAN
VERY LIGHT OPERA COMPANY**
Howard Conn Fine Arts Company
1900 Nicollet Ave. S.
Minneapolis, MN 55403
Tickets 612-925-9159

**THE HEART OF THE BEAST
PUPPET THEATER**
1500 East Lake St.
Minneapolis, MN 55407
Tickets 612-721-2535

HEY CITY STAGE
1430 Washington Ave. S.
Minneapolis, MN 55454
Tickets 612-333-1300

ILLUSION THEATRE
Bower Hawthorne Theatre
Hennepin Center for the Arts
528 Hennepin Avenue
Minneapolis, MN 55403
Tickets 612-339-4944

JUNGLE THEATER
709 W. Lake St.
Minneapolis, MN
Tickets 612-822-7063

LAKESHORE PLAYERS
6th St. & Stewart Avenue
White Bear Lake, MN 55110
Tickets 612-429-5674

LORING PLAYHOUSE
1633 Hennepin Avenue
Minneapolis, MN
Tickets 612-332-1617

**MINNEAPOLIS THEATRE
GARAGE**
2000 Lyndale Avenue South
Minneapolis, MN 55405
Tickets 612-870-0723

MIXED BLOOD THEATER
1501 South Fourth St.
Minneapolis, MN 55454
Tickets 612-338-6131

PARK SQUARE THEATRE
Minnesota Museum of Art
St. Peter & Kellogg Blvd.
St. Paul, MN 55101
Tickets 612-291-7005

PENUMBRA THEATRE CO.
Martin Luther King Bldg.
270 N. Kent St.
St. Paul, MN 55102
Tickets 612-224-4601

**PHIPPS CENTER FOR
THE ARTS**
109 Locust St.
Hudson, Wisconsin 54016
Tickets 715-386-8409

RED EYE COLLABORATION
15 West 14 St.
Minneapolis, MN 55403
Tickets 612-870-0309

SEVENTH PLACE THEATER
28 West 7th St.
St. Paul, MN 55101
Tickets 612-225-9002

THE SOUTHERN THEATRE
1420 Washington Ave. S.
Minneapolis, MN 55454
Tickets 612-340-1725

THEATRE DE LA JEUNE LUNE
P.O. Box 25170
Minneapolis, MN 55458
Tickets 612-333-6200

**UNIVERSITY CENTENNIAL
SHOWBOAT**
East River Flats Park
University of Minnesota
Minneapolis, MN 55455
Tickets 612-625-4001

VENETIAN PLAYHOUSE
2814 Rice St.
Little Canada, MN 55113
Tickets 612-484-1108

WALKER ART CENTER
725 Vineland Place
Minneapolis, MN 55403
Tickets 612-375-7622

WEYERHAEUSER AUDITORIUM
Landmark Center
75 W. 5th St.
St. Paul, MN 55101
Tickets 612-774-6699